A complementary therapy practice:
A practical guide

A complementary therapy practice: A practical guide

Viv Hinks

Quay Books

Mark Allen
Publishing Ltd

Quay Books Division, Mark Allen Publishing Limited,
Jesses Farm, Snow Hill, Dinton, Wiltshire, SP3 5HN

British Library Cataloguing-in-Publication Data
A catalogue record is available for this book

© Mark Allen Publishing Ltd 2000
ISBN 1 85642 140 6

Printed in the UK by Redwood Books, Trowbridge, Wiltshire

Contents

Acknowledgements and contributions

Sincere thanks to Di Wiggetts for her administrative support. For their help with various chapters I would like to thank:

* Nicola Evans of Evans Whalley for her contribution to *Chapter 8* on marketing

* Gabriel Mojay from the Institute of Traditional Herbal Medicine and Aromatherapy for his foreword

* Stephen Watling for his assistance with *Chapter 7*.

Foreword

The desire to heal, to be of benefit to the health and well-being of others, is an inherent virtue of the human soul. It is one that many of us become conscious of at a relatively young age – an aspiration that is often translated into a career in medicine or nursing. Yet the re-emergence of traditional systems of medicine, such as Oriental and Ayurvedic medicine, together with the rapid growth of relatively more novel approaches to natural healthcare, have meant that a new vocational arena has opened up. Those who feel 'called' to explore the career potentials of complementary medicine, in contrast to those who have trained in orthodox healthcare, are more likely to do so slightly later in life, when experience has taught them the limits as well as the benefits of medical science.

If life experience is a key factor in the decision to train in a chosen complementary therapy, so too is it an asset in the practice of that therapy. Such experience may embrace the personal, financial and professional dimensions of one's new career. Experience in relating to others in a professional or helping capacity is always of special value.

Yet despite the importance of motivation and experience, and of the expertise that we gain through training, setting up and maintaining a successful complementary therapy practice is as much a challenge as the mastery of one's healing art. Viv Hinks, in the pages of this book, demonstrates just this: that to succeed in a professional and business sense in complementary medicine requires dedicated attention and on-going development.

With her many years of experience as both a practitioner and teacher, Viv has considerable practical wisdom to share. Yet like all true teachers, she does so in a way that does not shirk difficult choices, and there are many that may form part of running a successful practice.

When choices can be made from a position of being well-informed about our options – whether, for example, to practice from home or from a clinic – we can maximise the potential of our therapeutic work where it may otherwise be curbed due to uncertainty or misconception. The balanced discussion of every important issue ensures that those who read this book will be empowered to succeed.

A professional practice in complementary medicine is both a joy and a responsibility. It is a joy to pursue a livelihood that is based on helping others, and an even greater joy to know that our work is benefiting their health. It is also a responsibility that involves a duty to one's clients, one's profession, and oneself. In each case, it is a duty that can only be fulfilled through the active cultivation of professionalism, ensuring that every aspect of one's practice is characterised by excellence.

If there is one sure step to achieving this outcome, I believe it lies in reading these pages. For however highly motivated and well-trained we may be, Viv Hinks has shown through *A Complementary Therapy Practice: A practical guide* that actually making it work requires specific knowledge, and has become an important area of learning in its own right. No one engaged in the study or the continuing professional development of a complementary therapy can afford to disregard it, not least if they aspire to fulfilling their greatest potential.

Gabriel Mojay
The Institute of Traditional Herbal Medicine
and Aromatherapy
March 2000

Introduction

This book is written from the perspective of a therapist who, having been in practice for many years, has learned by experience and not from the viewpoint of an expert business manager. Virtually every day sees the development of a new type of complementary therapy, which means that it is unfortunately beyond the scope of this book to address all the different types that are now available. It is recognised that different areas of therapy have different business needs. This is a general overview for complementary therapists and specific advice is given where possible. Generally, most information will be relevant to all therapists, possibly more so to 'bodyworkers' (practitioners who use contact/touch therapy, eg. massage or manipulation).

It is the aim of this book to provide a text that relates to developing the practice, rather than simply the ability to be a practitioner. Many therapists are adequately trained in their therapy but may not even be aware of the legal and business implications related to self-employment, using premises for the public, etc. It is important that we present a professional, reputable and stable image to both the public and orthodox health practitioners. Complementary and alternative medicine, known as CAM, is currently an enormous growth area. Therapies are now under close scrutiny and are undergoing academic and efficacy examination, as it is apparent that we, complementary therapists, are here to stay! The perception of complementary therapies has changed over the last 20-year period from being viewed as fringe, to being offered at degree and higher degree levels at universities. However, there is still prejudice and scepticism. Ability to maintain a practice and succeed within the business and professional arenas has probably never been more relevant.

Viv Hinks
May, 2000

1

Attitude and efficacy

Attitude

The therapist becomes a business person – is it possible? In a myriad of texts we are told that the caring, nurturing attitude of the therapist is vitally important. Furthermore, many people see the commercial side of the business as being in direct conflict to the therapeutic side. Over several years of training people in the complementary therapy world I have heard expressed the feeling, 'I can't take money for this', or, 'I can't charge money for that', over and over again. Some therapists see it as a kind of virtue if they are unable to ask for payment, but many believe that payment is a part of valuing the experience of the therapy. Some people might think that visiting a nurse, doctor, midwife or physiotherapist is free – but is it? Of course not; the public pays for the service. Ask any of the above if they would work for nothing and I'm sure you would hear laughter.

It is often the case that we recognise good advice and yet still find it hard to act on that advice, having to learn the hard way by our mistakes. An example from my own experience may help to illustrate this point about valuing yourself because, like all caring therapists, there are occasions when it seems difficult to ask a client for the full fee for a treatment.

A client (Mrs A) was attending my own aromatherapy practice for treatment to help with asthma caused by her working conditions. I liked Mrs A and we became friendly enough to exchange Christmas gifts. I learned that she had difficult family circumstances as well as suffering from ill health through her job. This client finally gave up her job as her work environment exacerbated her asthmatic condition. The aromatherapy treatments however, continued to help her to improve and she wanted to continue with them. As she was not working, for a considerable time I therefore charged her a negligible amount for treatments – not even enough to cover the cost of the oils, let alone the costs of the laundry, heating and my own valuable time. Perhaps you can imagine how my naive attitude changed when she told me she would be buying a bungalow in the country with some of her savings (some of which I had unwittingly contributed towards) while retaining her large city home.

This situation was not Mrs A's problem, it was mine and I decided from that day onwards that I would charge a reasonable professional fee, and would not subsidise other people's lifestyles. This does not mean that I only treat people with high disposable incomes. Inevitably, in the current structure of funding complementary therapies, according to HSBC's, 1998, business profile, 'customers' for therapies like aromatherapy are 'more likely to be female and have higher disposable incomes'.

Therapies can be covered by private health insurance plans or by company contracts. Some innovative companies sponsor employees with high stress levels to receive various therapies, including counselling.

Finally, if the client has a genuine need for the treatment but no way of affording to pay in cash, then perhaps you can exchange skills. In this way you might exchange a therapy treatment for your client's secretarial or gardening skills, for example. Using this method, there is a fairness and equality from both parties with neither exploiting the other.

So, we therapists have to earn a living. What possibilities are there? It is possible not to set up as a self-employed therapist but to research into other employment opportunities; you may find this in areas such as large corporate companies with occupational health suites, possibly employing therapists for stress-related problems, usually on a part-time basis. This trend may be on the increase: recent cases have shown that considerable financial compensation can be awarded to victims of work-related stress who pursue a claim through the courts. Some airlines are now employing therapists, such as reflexologists and aromatherapists for long haul flights or to treat jet lag on arrival. There is a growing area of possibilities of employment as complementary therapies grow in status and acceptance. Agencies now exist who supply therapy teams to nursing homes and care accommodation run by charities such as Sense, Mencap, Mind.

These agencies do employ staff, but if you put on your 'business head' you will probably find that your earning potential is much greater as a self-employed practitioner, negotiating directly with client groups. Attitude here is very important as if you are the type of person who needs security and are not easily motivated to find work for yourself, then employment versus self-employment is possibly a safer (even though less lucrative) option. Many people would find it very stressful to be dependent on constantly finding work, rather than to be on a regular salary.

There are certain personal characteristics that are important to being self-employed, and these do not relate to having business knowledge but they do need to be part of your individual character. Go through the list of questions in Chart A (*p.4*) and tick the points that you feel are true about yourself but be honest in your responses. If you can answer all the questions positively, you are likely to have what it takes to be self-employed. If there are a few questions you can't answer positively, you will have identified both your strengths and weaknesses and you can begin to work on the latter. More than a few negative answers would suggest that you would be better suited working for someone else rather than running your own business.

Whatever route to employment you follow, be clear from the start about your own worth. Owing to university fee structures, until recently many orthodox health practitioners may not have had to pay for their own training. Up until a few years ago, for example, nurses received a salary while they trained. This has never been the case with complementary therapy practitioners as their training will have cost the individual various amounts, depending on area, therapy and length of training.

Consider your time, not only contact training hours but also the many hours of additional home study, and the cost of your training needs or possibly long distance travel as it is rare to find the right courses on 'the doorstep'. When you have taken all this into consideration, as well as the start-up and running costs, this will give you some indication of why the practitioner should have no embarrassment in charging a reasonable fee! **Remember, if you don't value yourself no-one else will.**

Your own business desires will determine a considerable amount of what you achieve. Some therapists do not do their therapy any favours as they do not portray a professional image. If you believe that you are offering a professional therapy in its true sense, you would be unlikely, for example, to use a room at home, that doubles as a domestic room. Some therapists think that working from home is an easy or cheap option, without looking into the business aspects of this (see *Chapter 5*). In itself, working from home may not be ideal and if you attempt this in a room that is also a family room, or a spare bedroom, the image presented to the public will be wholly unprofessional.

Again, your attitude will dictate whether or not you will feel you can take on premises and risk committing yourself to a contract of some kind.

Many stories of disappointment and failure are heard concerning trying to establish a successful complementary health business. One therapist's prolonged catalogue of disasters was even given a full-page spread in the *Journal of the International Federation of Aromatherapists* (Stokes, 1998). The author gives her personal tale of woe. The article states that, 'Once you have qualified in your chosen field, the path to success is strewn with sceptics who question the efficacy of your treatments, gasp in shock at the cost of each session and think that because you are in a caring profession, you somehow don't need to make money like everyone else in order to live.' Preparation, patience and motivation are key factors in making a practice succeed.

In contrast, an example of a positive attitude to running a complementary health practice can be found in at the end of this chapter (*p.8*). Another inspiring example I have recently encountered is of a male reflexologist and aromatherapist who, despite being blind, has achieved relevant diplomas in each discipline at a further education college in Birmingham. Following this with an Enterprise Award from the local Enterprise Centre and a bursary from the Prince's Trust, this positive-minded young man has now started his own business using a specially adapted computer for his customer records.

Exercise/tick chart A

(Idea based on questionnaires from Business Link and enterprise agencies)

1. Your personality characteristics, are you:
   Logical, good at resolving problems and conflict? ☐
   Perceptive? ☐
   Organised and able to plan time? ☐
   Motivated? ☐
   An extrovert? ☐
   Confident and able to make decisions? ☐
   A good communicator, able to deal with those in authority,
   other health carers and consultants? ☐
   Sociable? ☐
   A good leader, able to negotiate and encourage? ☐
   Focused – but with the capacity to take advice and criticism? ☐
   Flexible, adaptable and open to evaluation? ☐
   An opportunist, a risk-taker and ambitious? ☐
   Hard working, committed? ☐
   Tough – having the ability to handle failures and rejection? ☐
   Individual – not afraid to be different? ☐
   Creative, imaginative? ☐
   Able to learn from mistakes? ☐
   Able to have some patience? ☐
   Able to value yourself? ☐

2. Are you in reasonable health? (Give yourself an honest appraisal.) ☐
   *If you have health problems, remember that running your own therapy
   practice will be demanding and time-consuming and most likely stressful!

3. Family commitments and support:
   Is your family or partner prepared for the impact of your employment ☐
   (for example, if you are to become self-employed,
   possibly with considerable business debts, is insecurity an issue?)
   Can you at least depend on moral support? ☐
   Can anyone within your family/support system invest in your ☐
   business or help support you financially in the 'quiet times'?

4. Do some preparation!
   Before you begin, visit several banks, Business Link, local Training Enterprise
   Council (TEC) and enterprise agencies.
   If your business may involve experiences that you are unfamiliar with (such as
   lone travel on long distances), undertake the experiences first to assess if you will
   cope.

5. Skills and qualifications:
   Professional therapy skills – vitally important to compete. Be the best you can be!
   You will find banks and business agencies are more favourable if you can show
   evidence of good training.
   Business skills – understand the principles of business planning and marketing.

Efficacy of therapies

A very important question you must ask yourself is: how well can you validate your practice? According to studies cited by Ernst (1996), most people have an understanding that certain types of complementary medicine are suited to specific complaints, ie. acupuncture for migraine, osteopathy for back pain, homeopathy for allergies etc. Equally they believe orthodox medicine to be by far the most efficient for problems associated with broken bones, bleeding etc. The more health options available, the more people shop around for health, trying out the various solutions or cures for different conditions.

Many people have stated that complementary medicine may have little more than a placebo effect (Kaptchuk *et al*, 1996). There can be little doubt that attitude can have a bearing on how well complementary therapy, complementary medicine or orthodox medicine works.

The following have all been stated as relevant to efficacy: expectation, persuasions, anticipation, belief, faith, suggestion, cultural beliefs, patient-practitioner relationship, imagination and conditioning. In order to 'prove' that a therapy has efficacy beyond the placebo effect numerous clinical trials with a blinding or double-blinding process have been carried out. The results do not always prove a beneficial effect. This may not be encouraging to the practitioner but it is important that each therapist is aware of negative as well as positive results and information, as the well-read and intelligent client may challenge the practitioner. This highlights the benefit of experience and empirical evidence.

If you are a midwife, you may be considering the integration of aromatherapy and reflexology into your practice in caring for pregnant women. Research trials to prove the efficacy of the former practice already exist; for example, in a study by Dale and Cornwell in 1994 the role of lavender oil in relieving perineal discomfort following childbirth was investigated. This was a blind randomised clinical trial with positive results over a 10-day period of use, showing a steady reduction in the discomfort scores (Dale and Cornwell, 1994). Also Denise Tiran, a principal lecturer in Complementary Therapies at the University of Greenwich, has written prolifically on complementary therapies within midwifery practice and has reviewed controversies as well as benefits (Tiran, 1996). As another example of ways in which orthodox and complementary therapies can interact, if you are considering training in cranio-sacral therapy with a particular interest in birth-trauma children, you should investigate these research trials. There are several texts which examine the efficacy and validity of complementary and alternative medicine (CAM), eg. Vickers, 1998; Jamil, 1997; and Ernst, 1996.

If the 'product' works, people will buy it. If your chosen therapy is a genuine healing process and provides relief for whatever disorder, your practice will thrive. By doing your homework and researching the efficacy of your product you will have the facts readily available to interested customers. Unfortunately, some practitioners have not helped the general image of complementary therapies by offering methods of treatment that are unreliable, controversial or subjectively suggested as beneficial, so a scientific and scholarly approach to your business will reassure potential clients that your therapy has an objective credibility.

According to Jamil (1997) certain therapies are more efficient with regard to treating different disorders. He also states that some conditions contra-indicate the use of certain therapies, stating that not all disorders 'caused by a serious underlying disease' are suitable for treatment by complementary therapies – no doubt many practitioners would disagree with that. Caring and responsible therapists take into account serious conditions and seek to complement orthodox treatment and enhance the quality of life for the patient.

Some examples, based on Jamil (1997) include:

* **Acupuncture**: is suitable for treating a wide variety of pain, including migraine, neuralgia, backache, bursitis and post-operative pain. Disorders such as Bells' palsy, vertigo, phobias and many physical conditions can be successfully treated. However, conditions where the patient has a blood condition, low platelet count or is undergoing warfarin therapy would not be suitable.

* **Osteopathy or Chiropractic**: are both extremely efficient for disorders such as back pain, joint pain and stiffness, whiplash injuries and repetitive strain injury. They may be contraindicated for patients who have had a previous unfavourable response to manipulation, or those with acute or unhealed fractures, certain bone diseases, vascular insufficiency of the vertebral artery or severe osteoporosis.

* **Reflexology**: is effective in treating muscular-skeletal pain, and helps alleviate psychological problems such as depression, insomnia and anxiety and progressive disorders; multiple sclerosis, Parkinson's disease and some gynae-cological disorders. However, reflexology is contraindicated for psychiatric patients on high dosage drugs, patients with severe fungal infections on their feet, inflammation or infection of veins or deep vein thrombosis.

* **Massage**: for treatment of muscular and joint pain, sports soft-tissue injuries, post-viral fatigue syndrome and psychological problems, including anxiety, stress and insomnia. Contraindications for massage include various infectious diseases, deep vein thrombosis and phlebitis.

Research to establish efficacy is of increasing importance; there is little benefit in training in any therapy only to find that it has been discounted by the scientific fraternity as invalid, or that the effect was purely placebo. Lewith (1998) states that, 'It is apparent that a substantial proportion of clinicians – complementary and conventional alike – do not base their practice sufficiently on the best possible evidence.' CAM practitioners need to understand why a certain treatment works and not simply give a treatment because that was how they were trained to do so. The greater our understanding and informed beliefs, the more likely we are to have a positive attitude and increased energy to put into our practice.

Exercises

1. Search data banks, journals, CD-Roms etc. for research trials done on the therapy that you practise or intend to practise.
2. When you start up your practice, log the positive and negative effects of your treatments, building up your own source of information.
3. Choose a disorder that you have a personal interest in and read everything you can find on complementary therapies for that disorder. You may well discover conflicting information and even research resulting in both success and disappointment.
4. Devise a questionnaire for your patients.

References

Dale A, Cornwell S (1994) The role of Lavender Oil in relieving perineal discomfort following childbirth: A blind randomised clinical trial. *J Adv Nurs* **19**: 89–96

Ernst E (ed) (1996) *Complementary Medicine: An objective appraisal*. Butterworth Heinemann, Oxford

HSBC Bank (1998) *Business Profile: Aromatherapy* No. 100: May 1998

Jamil T (1997) *Complementary Medicine – A Practical Guide*. Butterworth Heinemann, Oxford

Kaptchuk K, Edwards R, Eisenberg D (1996) Complementary medicine: Efficacy beyond the placebo effect. In: Ernst E (ed) *Complementary Medicine: an objective appraisal*. Butterworth Heinneman, Oxford: 42–70

Lewith G (1998) Misconceptions about research in complementary medicine. In: Vickers A (ed) *Examining Complementary Medicine*. Stanley Thornes, Cheltenham: 170–176

Stokes P (1998) Setting up an Aromatherapy Business. Aromatherapy Times, *J Int Fed Aromatherapists* **1**(39): 14–15

Tiran D (1996) The use of complementary therapies in midwifery practice: a focus on reflexology. *Complementary Therapies in Nursing and Midwifery* **2**: 32–37

Vickers A (1998) *Examining Complementary Medicine*. Stanley Thornes, Cheltenham

An example of a positive, motivated attitude from Barbara Thorpe, a practitioner from Solihull, Warwickshire

After 18 months of fascinating study, as a very mature student, I joined appropriate professional organisations and was ready to launch my new career as an aromatherapist, reflexologist and Reiki healer. Fortunately, I didn't have the problem of finding suitable premises, as during my training I had an extension built on my home, which I decorated and furnished with tranquillity as my theme.

So much for creating the right setting – now all I had to do was to bring in the clients! I decided to have an Open Day, to which I invited all my friends and colleagues with whom I had studied, plus everybody else I could think of, and asked them all to bring friends if they wanted to. I waited, wondering if anyone would actually turn up. To my delight they did and by the end of the day I had actually booked 11 appointments to get me off to a good start. I obtained lists from the library and wrote to all the local doctors saying I was writing in a spirit of co-operation and, if they had any patients who they felt might benefit from the therapies I offered, I would be very pleased to see them. I didn't really expect to get much response, but I have had a number of referrals.

During my training I had of course done case studies and after I became qualified I was very pleased to find that quite a number of them wanted to continue with their treatments. I had just about beaten the deadline for an advertisement in *Yellow Pages* and found that this brought quite a number of new clients. Naturally, I had a few odd calls, such as one asking for a massage in a hotel room at 3 am, but on the whole they were genuine enquiries and I have extended my client base quite considerably from this source. Giving talks and holding workshops can be another good way of attracting clients. The first time I was asked to give a talk at a large hotel for an audience of approximately one hundred, I said confidently yes of course I could do it, then put the phone down and panicked. However, it was a great success, and a couple of weeks later I did a workshop almost without any panic at all. If you believe in what you are doing, nerves seem to disappear.

The most satisfying way of building your practice is by personal recommendation. I have found that if you treat every person as someone special, give them all your attention, and provide treatments appropriate to their needs, they are eager to tell their families and friends. Gradually my client base is extending. I have a small poster in a local hair stylist's premises and I have offered a full body massage as an item to auction in aid of the local school. Use your initiative. The possibilities are endless, and the future looks bright.

2

Start-up procedure and planning ahead

Before a therapist gets to the point of starting a business or considering the future within his or her chosen profession, training and planning must have taken place. Before you commence any training, you would be well advised to consider the following points :

1. What are you really interested in?
2. What is the status of that therapy?
3. Is the market saturated or nearly saturated with practitioners or 'so-called practitioners' in that therapy?
4. In general, the more that you have to put in to your training the more you can expect to get out of it, ie. if your training has cost £30,000 and four years of your life, you should charge more for your treatments than if you have only invested in a 12-day training course.
5. What other expenses are involved during training besides paying for the training itself? For example, counsellors will have to pay for many hours private supervision during training and medical herbalists will have to pay for clinical supervision.
6. Do the best training that is available and that you can afford. If you do a basic level to start with, you must be prepared to do on-going training. Even after qualifying, many organisations insist on a minimum of two days per year postgraduate study (see *Chapter 3*).
7. Plan, early on, what you want to do with the training. If you want to take it into an area of the NHS, be clear that the level of training is acceptable to the policy in that area (see *Chapter 3*).
8. Check if there is a protected title or statutory title (eg. Registered Nurse, Chartered Physiotherapist) or if there is any move to protect that title. Also, is there a national register – if so, in both cases ensure that the training course leads to these criteria.
9. Contact the lead body/governing body and ask for a list of their accredited training establishments (see *Appendix I*, 'Useful addresses'). Contact several and check content and course fees, then the travelling distance involved and your own commitments such as work, childcare and other responsibilities.
10. If you plan to set up a practice 'from scratch', look around your chosen area, check *Yellow Pages*, clinics etc. What is available already? Will you be able to compete? (See *Chapter 8*.)

When these queries have been assessed, you should be well on the way to deciding which therapy you wish to practise.

At this juncture consider looking at the efficacy of the treatments. Research the feedback from clients and any research trails that have been done using the therapies. Assure yourself that there is a future in the therapy that you will practise (see *Chapter 1, pp. 3–4*).

Having decided on your field of therapy and training requirements, you should now consider the business aspect of earning a living as a practitioner. If you want to set up your own practice there are several steps you need to consider.

1. Market research:

- find out about competition in your locality and obtain as many price lists as you can
- find out about the availability and popularity of your chosen therapy in your locality
- find out what other competing treatments are available.

2. Research into legislation, regulations and codes of practice:

- what legislation governs the practice of your therapy?
- what health and safety regulations are applicable to your business?
- find out if there are any local authority provisions that may affect your business
- what organisations exist to support you in your chosen field and how would they help you in the setting up and running of your business?
- what codes of practice exist for your therapy?

3. Business options:

- what are the advantages and disadvantages of the business options available, eg. sole trader or partnership?

4. Business plan:

- it is essential that you produce a forecast for the first twelve months of your proposed business to see whether your plan is viable (see *Chapter 4*).

5. Acquisition and design of premises:

- find out what premises are available that are suitable for running your type of business, taking into account access, parking etc
- what legal formalities are involved in acquiring premises and what steps should you take to make sure that the premises are fit for your purpose?
- how would you design the layout of your practice? Produce a floor plan showing the amount of treatment rooms, reception area etc
- give examples of the type of decor you would use to promote the image of your business (you could provide small samples of materials/paper/colours chosen)
- if you are going to work from home, how might this affect your mortgage and home insurance, and what factors might contribute to a less than professional image? (See *Chapters 3* and *7*.)

6. Staff recruitment and management:

- finally, as you start, plan for the future: when will you need additional staff and if so will they be full time, part time or hired on a freelance basis?
- decide what it is you are looking for in your staff and provide a brief job description
- how would you go about finding suitable candidates and how would you decide who to choose?
- what would you need to consider if you were looking for a prospective future partner rather than just an employee?
- key personnel: who are they?
- determine what methods of employment are available, eg. paye etc, stating their respective advantages and disadvantages. Also, what legislation is involved?
- what do you need to do to be a good employer both through legislation and good management practice?
- what can be done to keep yourself and staff up-to-date with the latest products, practices and legislation?
- how do you keep your staff once you have invested heavily in them?
- how would you handle client complaints relating to staff and how would you train your staff to deal with clients?

7. Promotions (see *Chapter 8*):

- decide on a name for your business
- design your own unique logo
- investigate the best methods of announcing your business start-up
- consider what type of promotions you may be able to offer to encourage new clients
- design a price list
- design an advertisement to be placed in your local paper.

Many high street banks offer advice on setting up a business and another valuable source of help may be found at your local Business Enterprise Agency. These often produce information packs and some may even offer training courses on starting your own business. For more information about turning your business from an idea to a reality, see *Chapter 4*.

Exercises

1. Contact local agencies and attend a business-awareness seminar (which will probably be free).
2. Look at issues in *Chapter 1* and other chapters within this book before you proceed.

3. Write to relevant professional organisations with specific queries before deciding on your course of action.
4. Ask yourself the questions at the beginning of this chapter, ie. What is the status of the therapy? What are you actually going to do with the training?

Relevant draft units from the National Occupational Standards (NOS)

C1 Generate the business proposal

The elements of competence:

C1.1 Identify personal goals, needs and capabilities, which will affect the achievement of the proposed business.

C1.2 Explain the business and implementation idea.

C1.3 Identify the potential market and business trends that will affect the business venture.

The above requires the practitioner to:

- identify what they want from and will bring to the venture
- explain the business idea and what will be needed to put it into practice
- confirm that there is likely to be a sufficient market for the venture to operate successfully.

This unit is aimed at those who are thinking about setting up a small business.

C6 Plan the human resource development within the business

The elements of competence:

C6.1 Identify the personnel requirements to set up the business.

C6.2 Identify how the personnel requirements can be met.

C6.3 Plan how work will be allocated and evaluated.

C6.4 Plan how needs and opportunities for personal and staff development will be met.

The above requires the therapist to:

- identify skill and capability requirements needed
- plan to meet those needs
- decide how to share work and measure effective performance
- plan for future development.

This unit is aimed at those who are concerned with staffing and the development of the future business.

References

Birmingham Venture (1993) *Starting a Business in Birmingham.* Birmingham Chamber of Commerce Publication

National Occupational Standards (1997) *Consultation Pack, Section B; Setting up Practice Units.* Care Sector Consortium, distributed and written by Prime Research and Development Ltd, Harrogate

Team Training, Enterprise Link (1999) *Information on Starting a Business.* Team Training Services Ltd, Sutton Coldfield, Birmingham

3

Training

Training in complementary therapies may involve anything from a four-year full time degree course to a short correspondence course. The best advice one can therefore give is that it is advisable to examine carefully any new standards or moves toward Statutory Regulation, and a single national register in your chosen therapy. Gain assurance that your qualification will be recognised if regulatory processes exist or are being implemented and that the training would lead to inclusion in a National Register, if formed. Check that, if there is a lead body, the training course is accredited by that body. A lead body may be an 'umbrella organisation', which controls a number of professional organisations by criteria to which they all agree to conform, eg. number of training hours, length of training, etc. In the foreseeable future it is probable that a single regulatory body will be established for each therapy (see also *Chapter 10*).

It is currently often the case that more than one professional organisation exists for one area of practice (for example, see 'Training in aromatherapy', *pp. 16–21*, which presents the case for one selected complementary therapy). These different bodies are often in competition with each other and may not recognise each other's qualifications. There may also be political and/or financial reasons maintaining these diversities. This state of affairs is confusing for both the public and the prospective trainee. Future regulatory systems and conformity of training standards will help eliminate the disparity.

National Occupational Standards

The Care Sector Consortium published a pack of standards for the National Occupational Standards (NOS); these were intended for consultation among the profession and course providers in the late 1990s. These include an area exclusively dedicated to setting up a business in complementary therapy.

This has been written in a similar way to National Vocational Qualifications (NVQs) and outlines standards of competency. Relevant units (from the consultation pack written in 1997) are C1–C6 and summaries of appropriate units appear at the end of each correlating chapter. NOS are further discussed later in this chapter. More recently, Healthwork UK has been developing these standards; core therapies which have been involved in this development include aromatherapy, reflexology, hypnotherapy and homeopathy. Healthwork UK is a 'National Training Organisation' (NTO).

According to Healthwork UK, in 'A consultation document for the complementary medicine sector':

Healthwork UK is a new organisation, we do not hold predetermined views about how to engage with the complementary medicine sector. Up to now we have been listening to you, with the launch of this consultation document we are taking this process further.

May, 1999

The document continues, explaining (p.4):

Responsibility for National Occupational Standards and qualifications is shared between National Training Organisations and the regulatory bodies for qualifications. NTOs are responsible for the development of National Occupational Standards – benchmarks of competence and performance at work – which underpin qualifications. Where the standards are already in place, NTOs have a role in reviewing and promoting the standards, and advising on the structure of qualifications, including; NVQs and SVQs based on the standards. The responsibility for approving and procuring National Occupational Standards rests with the regulatory bodies for qualifications: QCA-Qualifications and Curriculum Authority, ACCAC-Qualifications, Curriculum, and Assessment Authority for Wales, and SQA-Scottish Qualifications Authority.

On reflection of the above, potential trainee therapists should consider if any course that they embark upon takes into account the basic framework of NOS.

According to Sylvia Baker (2000), 'NOS describe good practice and specify what needs to be achieved in the delivery of high quality services.' NOS provide a common reference point or language of good practice. She also states that they are not qualifications in themselves, and identifies other possible uses of NOS, such as:

- for professional purposes – a basis for criteria for professional registration, guides to good practice
- for personal and service development – importantly when considering training, NOS suggested use is as a basis for designing curricula and training courses.

NOS are subject to constant review and development. They are closely linked with the Qualifications and Curriculum Authority (QCA) and, for this reason, a potential student should be mindful of their integration into education and training programmes.

Training cost comparison

It must be emphasised that all of the following relate to lead body recognised professional training, **not** basic NVQ or general courses at further education colleges (which may be government subsidised).

Average length and cost (at the time of publication)

Therapy	Length of training	Cost
Aromatherapy Professional course recognised by AOC lead body	Approx. 12 months	£1,500 average
Cranio-sacral	18 months –3 years	Approx. £3,000
Crystal healing Affiliation of Crystal Healing organisation	Part time, 12 months	Approx. £800.00
Osteopathy British School of Osteopathy	3–4 years	£22,000
Reflexology	1 year	£1,000

Training in aromatherapy

Training to be a therapist in any of the areas of complementary therapies can be a minefield. Here, training in aromatherapy is used as an example.

Aromatherapy, in particular, has lately become an extremely popular therapy, often outgrowing its original roots in training: 'Complementary therapy is currently the fastest growing business in the UK, apart from the national lottery' (*Business Express*, 1998).

Seza Eccles, who was editor of *Aromatherapy Quarterly* for several years, wrote an editorial demonstrating the change in popularity since she qualified 10 years previously. The word, 'aromatherapy', having changed from virtually an unheard of therapy now seems close to saturation point in terms of the marketing use (or abuse) of the word 'aromatherapy' (Eccles, 1998). We can all identify with this, considering the washing-up and coffee commercials!

The enormous growth in popularity has brought with it a growth in the number of those wishing to be practitioners. However, many people have not been clear about their training route. Sadly, some people have opted simply for geographic convenience or cheapest training fees, without really exploring the emphasis, accreditation, standards or level of their chosen course.

Aromatherapy is still an emerging profession and does not have, as yet, a protected or chartered title. This leads to further confusion, both for the would-be therapist, the public and the practitioner. Anyone can currently call themselves an 'aromatherapist'. This state of affairs has led to people with no training at all setting up a practice with resultant problems.

As an emerging profession we need to identify what is an acceptable level of training and what is not. However, the UK is acknowledged as the world leader in aromatherapy. This position is due largely to the joint promotion of aromatherapy by the Aromatherapy Organisation's Council (AOC) and the Aromatherapy Trade

Council (ATC). Britain has led the world in having established self-regulatory bodies for the profession and the essential oil trade (Baker, 1999).

In fact, aromatherapists all over the world look to Britain and the AOC as a role model for development of the profession. So what is the AOC? The AOC is the UK governing body for aromatherapy, representing 12 professional associations and around 6,000 aromatherapists. It has established minimum standards and a core curriculum for training courses that include (very briefly):

- anatomy and physiology
- common ailments
- the origins, chemistry and therapeutic properties of 30 essential oils
- blending and mixing essential oils
- therapeutic massage
- safety
- detailed consultation procedures
- referral procedures
- business and legal matters
- a minimum of 210 hours over a minimum of nine months.

These are the absolute minimum standards according to the AOC and many of the organisations and individual training establishments have much more in-depth standards than these.

A qualified aromatherapist should belong to one of the AOC's 12 member professional associations (AOC). The 12-member professional organisations that belong currently to the AOC are:

- Aromatherapy and Allied Practitioner's Association (AAPA)
- Association of Holistic Practitioner's International (AHPI)
- Association of Medical Aromatherapists (AMA)
- Association of Natural Medicine (ANM)
- Association of Physical and Natural Therapists (APNT)
- English Société de L'institut Pierrre Franchomme, France (ESIPF)
- Guild of Complementary Practitioner (GCP)
- Holistic Aromatherapy Foundation (HAF)
- International Federation of Aromatherapists (IFA)
- International Society of Professional Aromatherapists (ISPA)
- Register of Qualified Aromatherapists (RQA)
- Renbardou Institute (RI).

(AOC 1)

The curriculum and standards are constantly revised, and the qualified aroma-therapists belonging to these organisations have received a professional training.

There are other routes of training in aromatherapy and a large area comes under the beauty therapy arena. The qualifications and curriculum authority (QCA) recognised a major loophole in May, 1998. Aromatherapy was (and still is) seen as an aspect of beauty therapy developed by the Health and Beauty Therapy Training Board (HBTTB) and, as such, was offered as a Level 3 NVQ

'Aromatherapy Massage'. This caused great confusion, as many people mis-understood the holistic health approach (incorporating clinical applications) with the beauty therapy approach (incorporating aesthetic applications).

In May 1998 the QCA announced that, 'There will no longer be a full Level 3 NVQ in Aromatherapy Massage instead there will be a Level 3 NVQ in Beauty Therapy incorporating Aromatherapy, in the form of a single unit, " Treat client using Aromatherapy body massage".' This will be one of four optional units and candidates must select and complete three to achieve the full NVQ (Beauty Therapy).

Another training route is offered by a multi-disciplinary, non-governing body: the Vocational Awards International (VAI). This is a charitable trust and, according to their information literature, they offer a wide diversity of qualifications, including first aid, manicure, nail art, ear piercing, beauty therapy, aromatherapy, reflexology, fitness and sports therapy. The qualifications can lead to membership of organisations such as The International Institute of Health and Holistic Therapies (IIHHT).

Although not members of the AOC, these organisations are frequently offered at further education colleges and attract funding. The standard for the VAI Aromatherapy diploma is a little unclear but is around NVQ Level 3.

In their information the VAI claim that this is the major international qualification in its field (VAI1). Obviously there is some conflict and discrepancy between the various organisations.

Similarly, the International Therapeutic Examination Council (ITEC) offer an Aromatherapy diploma. Although not equivalent to an NVQ level, it is offered at some further education colleges, and ITEC is a multi-disciplinary examination body, offering vocational qualifications in a plethora of different therapies. The ITEC curriculum and content have been considerably upgraded since 1995.

Many adult education (Ad Ed) classes offer subjects such as aromatherapy, but clearly as adult education is frequently offered as a 12-week course, or very occasionally over one year (approximately 30 weeks over 3 terms, around 1½ hours a week – 45 hours in total) the content can in no way match the required professional criteria. Adult education in this area should be seen as an intro-duction, not as a professional training, but possibly as a basis for individuals to use aromatherapy themselves or with their family. It could be argued that offering therapies at adult education classes is itself controversial, as the facilities are usually inadequate, with no couches or privacy. Such inadequacy can lead to health and safety issues when giving treatments as the lack of an appropriate height couch or plinth could lead to back strain and possible injury. Privacy is also vital when people are partially removing clothing: a lack of privacy can lead to embarrassment, stress and inhibition, all of which are negative feelings and would be better avoided. Lack of privacy and 'client dignity' is also unprofessional and does nothing for the image of the therapy. Having been an adult education tutor some years ago in Birmingham and acting as an external moderator, I feel that there is possibly a case against offering such therapies, as it could also be thought to challenge the professionalism of aromatherapy. We don't see adult education classes in physiotherapy, dentistry or chiropody, do we?

Finally, there are now academic routes available. Several universities offer degree level in courses in CAM (see *Chapter 10*). These can only be beneficial for the general status of aromatherapy and other CAM professions as they underpin the theory with clinical practice and research projects.

It would be impossible to cover all training routes here, but the main routes are mentioned, with the exception of any correspondence courses. Because no correspondence courses are accredited by the major professional organisation identified, this does not mean that they haven't created their own organisation. I think though that most people would agree that there is no comparison between the benefits of face-to-face training and distance learning in a subject that involves a large area of practical skills, interaction and development of the therapeutic relationship.

As an exercise consider the following, and be completely honest with yourself:

* If we want to develop aromatherapy into a true profession can we justify correspondence courses or a few weeks training?

* If a client asks you about your standard of training, are you comfortable with it?

* Does a programme that covers the use of around 15 oils compare to one that covers 40–50 oils? For example, detailed information on a minimum of 40 essential oils is studied in the courses accredited by the Register of Qualified Aromatherapists (RQA) (under the AOC umbrella). (RQA1)

* Can you identify essential oils by their botanical names?

* Are you familiar with the exact species you are using, its chemical constituents and its therapeutic effects?

* Have you been trained to the level that you wish to work at; for example, with people with cancer or with pregnant women?

* Just as importantly, have you checked that your professional insurance covers you for all areas of your practice? (Some will have specific exclusions.)

* If you want to work abroad does your insurance cover you outside the UK and is your qualification recognised?

* Are you aware that a diploma does not necessarily mean a Diploma in Higher Education (DipHE)? A professional diploma can be studied that does not necessarily equate to the DipHE; also sadly any 'Peter Pan' organisation or training establishment can give a certificate or diploma.

Remember that 'credits' from one awarding body may not equate to credits from another professional or academic body.

Think back to your training, or reflect on your potential course – do you think any one person is an expert in all areas? Courses have developed now to a level where several tutors/lecturers are involved in the delivery of the course.

Also, is there a criteria that the aromatherapy teacher has practitioner experience? For example, to become an IFA principal teacher you need five years of practitioner experience. Ask yourself these questions and reflect on different standards of training.

In 1998 the National Occupational Standards (NOS) were published for aromatherapy after a three-year government funded project in which many practitioners were involved. The Independent Care Organisation (ICO) is a national umbrella organisation, which was responsible for the development of NOS. NOS have continued to be developed by health agencies; see illustrations of units throughout this book.

The AOC was granted the first Complementary and Alternative Medicine (CAM) independent seat on the ICO in 1996. Such independent seats are reserved for organisations that can demonstrate that they are the acknowledged leading body for their therapy (Baker, 1999).

These NOS may soon be in place and are expected to come out at NVQ Level 4, so as to distinguish them from 'Beauty Therapy' Level 3 (AOC2).

Many training organisations have already taken these NOS into account, but it should be recognised that many people do not like the NVQ 'Competence' style frameworks and although standards may be 'integrated', style and programmes may be more academic and/or professional than vocational.

On the very close horizon we have 'Statutory Regulation of title for Aromatherapists'. In March 1999 a working party was set up by the AOC (AOC3). The process is currently under way to fall in line with expected NHS proposals (AOC4). In the future, this regulation should clarify who has been adequately trained and who has not. It is also imminent that a national register will be created, which again will be of great benefit to the public as well as the profession. The idea of a single national register has been with us for some years. A British Directory of Aromatherapists was agreed by the AOC Council in 1995 (AOC4). In November 1998, Gabriel Mojay presented a paper at the Aroma-therapists Forum in London (Mojay, 1998), clearly demonstrating the value and necessity of this, and this procedure is now in hand. There may be different levels of registration, eg. associate and full, or assistant and practitioner.

To conclude, this is a huge area and it would not be feasible to cover every single aspect, but this chapter gives an overview or a distinct 'aroma' of the current situation. Some things must continue to change in order to present a clear, well-presented profession to the public (see *Chapter 10*).

All AOC organisations insist on two days a year postgraduate courses. If you are looking for postgraduate training, choose courses that really help you; so be prepared to travel and to look at courses all over the country to upgrade your knowledge.

Remember there is no such thing as the **perfect course** but some are definitely better than others and some courses may be better suited to your needs than others.

It is also obvious to me that some excellent therapists can be produced from less than excellent courses, and that some incompetent therapists can be created by an excellent course – it's the person that counts.

Exercises

1. Contact the lead body of your chosen therapy (see *Appendix I*, 'Useful addresses').
2. Compare different courses for content and cost.
3. Check for the popularity and efficacy of the therapy and consider how you would conduct a feasibility study.

References

Aromatherapy Organisation Council 1 Information from the AOC publicity leaflet *Your Concerns are Our Concerns*. AOC, London

Aromatherapy Organisation Council 2 (1999) (Document) '*The AOC Keeps All Options' Open Paper*. AOC, London

Aromatherapy Organisation Council 3 (1999) (Document) *Report on Statutory Regulation of Title*. AOC, London

Aromatherapy Organisation Council 4 (1999) (Document) *The History and Structure of the AOC*. AOC, London

Baird A (1998) Statement. *Business Express,* Autumn: 19

Baker S (Update February 1999) 1 + 2 (PR Chairman) AOC

Baker S (2000) National Occupational Standards (NOS) in aromatherapy. *Holistic Therapist* Aug/Sept: 9

Eccles S (1998) Editorial. *Aromatherapy Quarterly* **57**: 5

Healthwork UK (1999) *Standards and Qualifications – A Consultation Document for the Complementary Medicine Sector*. Healthwork UK, National Training Organisation, London

Mojay G (1998) AOC Conference Proceedings, *One Practice, One Profession*. AOC, London

National Occupational Standards (1997) *Development of N.O.S. for Aromatherapy Practitioners*, Section B: Consultation Pack of Standards: 9–130; *Setting Up Practice* Units are the same for all core therapies having NOS written for the Care Sector Consortium: November

RQA 1– RQA Booklet – *Objectives, Rules and Constitution*. Register of Qualified Aromatherapists, Chelmsford, Essex

Vocational Awards International 1(1997) *VAI Document Q2*: 8. Vocational Training Charitable Trust, PO21 2PN

4

Business and financial planning

It is money well spent to consult an accountant at the earliest stage of your planning. He or she can advise you on your personal and projected financial position and may be the best person to introduce you to a solicitor who specialises in business affairs. If you do not have an accountant, your bank manager will be able to advise you on local ones operating in your area. In any event you should speak to your bank manager, who can give you a great deal of useful information about setting up a business.

A good accountant will cost you a reasonable fee. He or she will help with compiling accounts, completing income tax self-assessment and returning taxation documents to the Inland Revenue. This annual outlay may seem considerable when you first start up your business, but this investment could save you thousands of pounds a year as your workload increases. You will be able to simply hand over everything to do with the financial aspect of your business to the accountant, to do what he or she does best and thus allowing you to do what you do best in your field of complementary health. In fact, as a general rule, it is part of good business practice to employ other businesses to help you with specialist areas. Due to the complicated nature of finances, seek out a recommended and reputable accountant.

It is more advantageous for very small businesses to operate on a sole trading basis from the tax point of view. A booklet entitled *Starting Your Own Business* (CWL1) is available from your local Inspector of Taxes, Contributions Agency or HM Customs and Excise. This booklet explains what you need to do when you start in business, and deals with income tax, national insurance and VAT. If you have been in previous employment you will also need the form P45 given to you by your last employer.

When you set up your business as a sole proprietor or as a partnership your national insurance position will be different to that of an employee. As a self-employed person you are responsible for paying your national insurance contributions yourself. Two leaflets, NI41 (*National Insurance Guide for the Self Employed*) and NP18 (*Class 4 Contributions*) can be obtained from your local DSS office and these will give details of your contribution requirements. You can also notify the office of your change of status to a self-employed person by completing the form in the NI41 leaflet.

Registration for VAT

An accountant can best advise you on this subject. You will only have to register for VAT if your taxable turnover (not profit) is likely to exceed the VAT registration figure. If your turnover does not exceed this amount there is no need for you to register for VAT. The pamphlet *Should I Be Registered for VAT?* is available from your local Customs and Excise office and clearly outlines the VAT requirements.

Working from home

In addition to the income tax rules covering self-employment, any person working from home needs to consider the possible implications for Capital Gains Tax. Booklet *CGT11* (p.17) and booklet *IR123* (p.12) from the Inland Revenue will give you guidance on these points. If you have a mortgage on your home, prior to April 2000 any business use may mean your loan attracts business loan rates and not domestic loan. The MIRAS scheme has previously given tax relief on mortgage loans. This is now no longer available (see *Chapter 5*).

Your business plan

All new businesses must have a viable business plan in order to access funding. Therefore, many of the sections within this book will cover the items needed for such a plan.

There are different styles of business plan but the following inclusions are fairly standard. The plan can be divided into the following areas:

- introduction
- resources
- the market
- finance
- the future
- appendices.

Under these broad headings, a number of more precise topics should be included.

Introduction

a)   A table of contents, with page numbers indicated.

b) Summary:
- a brief account of the business, including a clear description of the product/service
- the people involved, numbers etc, markets to be aimed at, legal status of the business, start-up costs and total funding requirement.

c) A description of the people involved; personal profile of the main skills and experience of the key personnel, summarising their CVs. Description of role and responsibilities in the new business.

d) Aims: business objectives of the entrepreneur and personal expectations.

Resources

a) Details of premises: legal and statutory requirements, including rent, service charges, length of lease, layout, location, size and usage, physical alterations and refurbishment required.

b) Service or products: production methods or service delivery. Staff policy and wages, health and safety and insurance.

c) Suppliers, credit terms and stock control.

The market

a) Market research undertaken: analysis and conclusions about customers and the competition.

b) Marketing strategy: Proposed methods of selling. Marketing, advertising and promotion.

c) Any sales/orders achieved to date.

Finance

a) Start-up costs to include: premises, equipment, vehicle, stock, publicity, insurance and sundries. Clarification on whether the items are being introduced into the business as assets already owned, or as a cash contribution, or require funding from outside sources.

b) Breakdown of funding sought, expected source and progress to date.

c) Break-even analysis.

d) Assumptions behind sales projections, receipts and payments. Pricing policy and credit terms.

e) Cash-flow forecast for the next six months and a further year where appropriate.

The future

Realistic assessments of the medium term prospects of the business.

Appendices

a) CVs of all key personnel, including details of past employment responsibilities, qualifications, skills and background. Any other directorship and business interests.

b) Extract from the lease of business premises, if relevant.

c) Certificate of incorporation, if a limited company.

d) Up-to-date management accounts and end of year accounts.

As with any planning, it is a case of thinking before you begin.

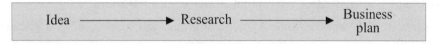

Idea ⟶ Research ⟶ Business plan

Your idea will include which therapy you have chosen and the style of practice you wish to set up. Research will be finding out about possible clients/consumers. Who are they? Where are they? What do they want? Who are your suppliers? Which suppliers have the most favourable terms for you?

Sources of information include professional organisations, chambers of commerce, enterprise agencies, accountants, training enterprise councils, banks and professional insurance brokers.

If you do not plan you are unlikely to succeed.

Finance

Consider:

- start-up costs, ie. equipment, initial outlay for remedies etc
- banking arrangements
- cash-flow
- pricing policy
- government requirements: taxation, national insurance and other costly legal responsibilities
- simple book-keeping: keep a simple record of income and expenditure. For example, retain bank statements, banking records, receipts, invoices, sales and purchase, mileage record for business travel.

Remember that many government agencies give inexpensive or free help to small businesses that are starting up. Funding is also often available and agencies such as Enterprise Link will be able to point you in the right direction.

What finance may be available?

In January 1999 The Bank of England's quarterly report, *Finance for Small Firms,* stated that, 'Small firms are now more appropriately financed than in the early 1990s.'

Funding changes on a regular basis, and availability may depend on when you apply and how many funds are available. Funding is usually a grant, a loan or a package. Examples of possible funding include:

Enterprise awards: These are available to new businesses, through enterprise agencies. These awards are grants as opposed to a loan, and therefore do not have to be repaid. An enterprise agency is one which provides information and access to resources to businesses; for example, Business Link Birmingham Enterprise.

Enterprise link venture fund: A range of financial support in one package including:

- loan interest relief up to a certain percentage of the loan
- rent guarantee or deposit
- crime prevention grant
- a basic start-up grant
- health and safety grant, and others through Enterprise Link.

Banks: They may make an overdraft facility available on your business account. Overdrafts are possibly less favoured by banks than they used to be. 'Packaged loans' have replaced them to some extent. Many small businesses do, however, like the flexibility of an overdraft facility as a 'fall back' position. Many high street banks have a 'small business manager', and all have an advice pack to new businesses and offer an introductory attraction, such as 12–18 months free banking.

It is important to shop around between different banks before you open your business account. It is usually necessary to have a business account before any funds will be paid to you, such as a business grant or loan. Some banks work with an agency to provide a 'soft loan'. This will have a preferred rate of interest and may not require security. Examples of such loans are:

* Bank/Enterprise Link loan fund or a joint loan scheme. These schemes may offer flexibility to finance working capital for a variety of purchases or assets.

* Local City Council Economic Development. These may offer small grants, for such items as:
    - business plan development
    - market research
    - marketing and promotion
    - exhibitions
    - product development
    - expansion and larger awards for job creation.

* The Prince's Youth Business Trust. This is nationwide, sponsored by HRH The Prince of Wales. It is available (currently) to 18–30-year-olds, and can

award both loans and grants. The Trust gives priority to the unemployed, but will consider any young person who has a viable business proposal.

* The National Lottery. If you wish to start a therapy project 'for the public good' and not for private gain, it may be possible to obtain an award from the National Lottery.

Once your business is up and running, different funding may be available to you. For example:

Small Firms Loan Guarantee Scheme (SFLG): This helps businesses that lack security to obtain a loan, sometimes with a capital repayment holiday.

Small Firms Training Loans: High street banks offer loans to cover training costs for small businesses.

Regional Selective Assistance: Various levels of grants are available from the Department of Trade and Industry (DTI) if you are starting a business in a development area which will create new employment.

Venture Capital: A financial institution that has a share in your business by providing capital (details available from Enterprise Link Agencies).

'Business Angels': These are private investors who may wish to invest and then share in future profits. A directory is kept by Enterprise Link Agencies.

Other funds for both start-up and expansion are available, such as European funds and competitions, eg. 'Livewire' supported by Shell UK, for young people under 30 with new business ideas. Special funds are often available in different areas, and you can find out about them through Enterprise agencies and banks.

Areas which are assisted by European Social Funds may offer assistance for charitable projects, which may enable therapy to be provided where the client could not otherwise access it because of resources and finance. See *Figure 4.1, overleaf* for cash flow forecast.

Exercises

1. Approach three high street banks and ask for their information packs on starting a small business. Investigate their required style of business plan and interest rates on business borrowing.
2. Enquire at your local city council about what their economic development department can offer new businesses.
3. Contact your Inland Revenue office and request the information leaflets listed under 'References'.

Work done: Month	1	2	3	4	5	6	7	8	9	10	11	12	Total
Cash sales/treatments													
Credit sales													
Grant/loans/cash introduced													
Total receipts													
Materials/stock													
Advertising/publicity													
Telephone													
Printing/stationery													
Repairs/maintenance													
Travel/vehicle costs													
Accountancy/legal													
Sundries													
Wages/salaries (staff)													
Rent/rates													
Power/light													
Insurance													
Bank charges													
Bank interest													
PAYE/NI													
Drawings													
Loan payments													
VAT													
Capital expenditure													
Total payments													
Movement													
Opening balance													
Closing balance													

Figure 4.1: Cash flow forecast

Relevant draft units from the National Occupational Standards (NOS)

C3 Plan the business operation

The elements of competence:

> **C3.1** Produce a business plan for the proposed business venture.
>
> **C3.2** Plan the implementation of the business proposal.

The above requires the therapist to:

- produce a business plan
- produce an implementation plan.

This unit is aimed at those responsible for making the business proposal into a firm plan.

C5 Determine the requirements for monitoring and controlling business operations and quality

The elements of competence:

> **C5.1** Identify resource requirements for the business.
>
> **C5.2** Identify ways to monitor and control the provision of products and services by the business.
>
> **C5.3** Determine the quality criteria and quality control procedure.

The above requires the therapist to:

- identify the resources needed to operate
- establish effective monitoring and control systems
- establish quality criteria and systems.

This unit is aimed at those responsible for establishing new quality criteria and control of the business.

References

Inland Revenue, Contributions Agency and HM Customs & Excise (1998) *CWL1 Starting your own Business?* HMSO, London

Inland Revenue (1996) *Mortgage Interest Relief IR123*. HMSO, London

National Occupational Standards (1997) *Consultation pack, section B; Setting up Practice* Units. Care Sector Consortium, London

Inland Revenue (1998) *Capital Gains Tax CGT*. HMSO, London

Team Training Enterprise Agency (1999) *Start up Business Literature*. Team Training Services Ltd, Sutton Coldfield, Birmingham

5

Venue

During training would-be therapists often envisage themselves working from home, possibly visualising a comfortable, quiet room that they have refurbished in therapeutic furnishings and colours. The main attraction may well be one of two prominent possibilities:

- it may seem cheap or even free
- it may give freedom to fit in other personal and domestic tasks during the working day.

There are several possible options of where to set up practice and working from home should be viewed in the same light as other venues by weighing the advantages against the disadvantages. Under the heading 'Codes of practice' we will consider the basic necessities of the practice area; however, the treatment area should also be considered here. If you wish to set up a professional practice with a professional image, you should never use a room in your home that doubles for domestic purposes. Imagine the poor impression made by a therapy room in which the couch has to vie for space with bedroom furniture. Horror stories abound of, for example, aromatherapists advertising full professional treatments but whose clients may arrive at their home address only to be shown into the kitchen or dining room and told to undress and get onto the table.

Any therapists behaving in this manner do their therapy a gross disservice.

Guidelines for the treatment room

* The room should be used solely for professional therapy treatments, although not necessarily one therapy, as various people may share a room in a clinic or possibly one therapist may offer several therapies.

* The room should be private and allow for confidentiality and modesty.

* The room should be well lit, but not with glaring overhead lights.

* The treatment area should be well ventilated and draught-free.

* The temperature should be comfortably warm.

* Noise levels: although it is inevitable that some sounds will filter through, you should ensure that noise levels do not become a disturbance as, whatever therapy you practice, a relaxed client will benefit more from the treatment.

* The room should be of a size that allows for basic equipment and comfort.

* Toilet and washing facilities should be adjacent to the room.

The workplace

Working from home

The advantages

1. Relatively inexpensive, as you are already paying rent, mortgage and/or overheads.
2. You do not have to consider possible increases from the landlord.
3. There may be some tax benefits – part of the costs of heating, lighting and telephone can be deductible for business expenses.
4. Convenient and saves commuting time, which can then be spent on the business itself.
5. Possible help from your family or those you live with – perhaps with answering the telephone, secretarial tasks or simply as another person in the background for safety.
6. Possible intimate, friendly and homely atmosphere that may enhance therapies, such as counselling or relaxation and stress management therapy.
7. You may be able to fit in domestic or personal activities during your professional day.
8. If you have children, you are physically in the house while they can be in another part of the house, secure in the knowledge that you are there (provided that they are old enough to be safe without your supervision).
9. Your home may well offer you a space to keep your own things – such as towels, oils, remedies, crystals and needles – which you would otherwise have to transport.
10. You can choose how you want to arrange the room, its layout, colours and equipment.

The disadvantages

1. It may not be as cheap as you first think. For example, if you charge a large portion of your household bills to the business you risk payment of capital gains tax, on any profit you make on the sale of your home. Also, the business will incur other taxes (see under 'Finance' in *Chapter 4, pp.25–27*) and legal payments, which, if you work outside the home, would be paid by the owner of the clinic/practice.
2. You will **most likely** need planning permission if there is a 'change of use' of the building, which clearly means that if it is not already a therapy clinic you need to get planning consent. If you intend to carry out any structural alterations you will also need planning permission. Although there does not

appear to be a hard and fast ruling on working from home (according to Birmingham City Council Department of Planning and Architecture, for example), there are several things to consider. In the booklet produced by Birmingham City Council, *Home Based Work Activity: All you need to know,* section 4.2 is probably the nearest reference to a complementary therapy practitioner. 'Medical services' examples given are chiropodists and physio-therapists where planning consent is required when a number of rooms are used. Key issues that are likely to affect most people include the amount of off-street parking available (section 6.1) and if there would be a change, altering the predominantly residential character of the area. If you have people attending your home for appointments, this changes the nature of your home from residential to business, eg. you may also need to display a plaque and have deliveries made, and make alterations to accommodate business visitors. Remember that you may think your business will not affect anyone around you, but your neighbours may well see things differently. Section 7.1 suggests that planning consent may be required for the display of a business, trade or professional sign. Again, remember that for many therapies under the code of conduct/practice, this display is essential.

3. If you rent your home your landlord may object to the use of his property as a base for your business; this may mean a rent increase, that a specific exclusion may exist or that you may even have to move home if you contravene your lease.

4. If you have a mortgage on your home you must inform the bank or building society as there may be a specific exclusion on the property being used for business purposes or possibly a clause on the deeds, especially in certain areas.

5. Insurance (see also *Chapter 7*): if you run a business from home your insurance will be affected. Home contents insurers must be informed and buildings insurers must be contacted too. Failure to do this could very likely invalidate any claims you make.

6. Privacy and home life – for many of us exposing our family and home to the public, and vice-versa, is not acceptable. Normal family life involves activity, dirt and noise and it can be difficult to keep this from your clients and equally difficult and unfair to suppress your normal family life.

7. Animals – not only does it contravene all kinds of hygiene and practice codes to have an animal anywhere near the vicinity of treatments, some clients may also have an allergy to or terror of certain animals. Hearing barking or seeing a cat as they ring the bell could do damage to their attitude to the treatment session!

8. Most councils have some form of licensing for premises offering any kind of massage or body work (see *Chapter 6, pp.49–51*). If this is payable – for example, if you are an aromatherapist working at home – you must obtain a license and pay the full annual fee.

9. If you are alone in your home and have the public coming to your house, you are making yourself vulnerable in several ways, with regard to both personal safety, legal safety and protection of your property (see 'Advice/discussion' *pp.34–35*).

10. Business Rates: this is different from council tax. The amount businesses pay is assessed by the value of the business premises. If you have a private residence that you then use a part of for business, that area is liable to payment.
11. Consider who has access to the telephone. If a client phones will it be a child or a non-professional voice that answers?
12. The image of the practitioner who works from home may be less professional than their clinic-based counterpart. Therapists may appear sloppy, harassed or distracted if they are fitting in domestic responsibilities within the professional day.
13. Advertising: working from home means that the public has your private address.

Working from home: advice/discussion

If you organise a clinic from home, try and avoid the temptation of doing this covertly, eg. not applying for planning consent , or not declaring a business on your home insurance. It could be tempting to take the easier and cheaper option, but in the long run this will not help you. For example, if you do not use your treatment room exclusively for therapy you may not have to pay business rates (although that is not definite and depends on each council district valuer). Insurance of all kinds, contents, public liability etc. may be invalidated if you omit to mention that you run a business from home. Also, you may not have to pay capital gains tax on the sale of the house if room/s have been used non-exclusively for business purposes. These sound economically attractive options, but remember to consider professional codes of conduct, professional image and perceived value of a therapy offered in a domestic room.

Think of the reality of your home: if you have clients visiting you will need to keep all areas where the public go extremely tidy and hygienic. Also remember that cooking odours linger, so you must take care about food smells if you are practising from home the same or the following day that you have been cooking. This does not mean that these areas can't be domestic and therapeutic, but they certainly can't have dog hairs, children's skates, dirty washing etc. in evidence. Noise is also a real issue if you have children in the house; it is unfair and unrealistic to expect children to be kept quiet.

If you decide to start up at home, the ideal situation for a treatment room is on the ground floor, as near as possible to the front door, or, if possible, a separate side entrance. It might be physically impossible for some clients to negotiate stairs, thus making an upstairs treatment room or toilet facility impractical. Have a waiting area in the hallway, in case of any timing problems or delays. Be aware of your property and make everything as secure as possible where your clients may be waiting. It is safer in every way to put valuables away (this also stops unfair suspicion). You must also have a toilet and washing facilities available for your client, to comply with codes of practice, and you may contravene safety issues if a client has to go up and down stairs to use facilities.

As for the telephone, my advice would be to get a separate line solely for business use. One of the main problems already discussed with working from home is a lack of privacy. Clients phoning you on your home line is extremely disruptive at any time and can be unpleasant. A separate business line (for which you pay business prices and get free listing in business telephone books) allows you to have a business answer-phone and maintain a professional image, and means that you simply do not answer that designated telephone out of business hours. A word of warning: complementary therapy practitioners are well-trained, professional individuals, but, as we provide a public service, it is not uncommon to receive unpleasant or even obscene messages left on answer-phones. This is particularly relevant to massage therapists and aromatherapists. If you work from home, be sure to have a separate line that is not answered by your children.

Mobile therapy practice

The advantages

1. No premises overheads – and all the benefits that go with that.
2. Wider geographical clientele possibilities: you can get to those who would not come to your practice because of lack of transport or inclination.
3. You can visit sick, elderly or infirm clients who would otherwise not be able to receive a treatment.
4. Complete freedom of when you work, without consideration of clinic room availability, domestic noise and family activity.
5. You can fit in other activities while you are visiting your clients, possibly seeing friends, visiting the supermarket, banking etc. Time management is far more flexible.
6. Certain legal aspects, such as licensing, do not apply as it is the premises not the individual that is licensed.
7. All your car costs, maintenance, as well as usual business expenses, will be tax deductible.

The disadvantages

1. You need a reliable car and car insurance for business use. This is absolutely necessary and will cost more. Your car will also take considerable wear and tear, internally and externally, plus you will clock up more mileage.
2. It can be physically demanding to carry equipment; for example, if you need to take a portable therapy couch in and out of your car, coverings, towels and/ or robes for clients. Also, you may need to transport oils, bottles, comfort cushions plus portable music player and CDs if you wish to create a certain ambience.
3. You have no control over the environment in which you are going to give a treatment.Your client may wish you to treat them in their noisy dining room or in the intimate privacy of their bedroom (both may be equally intimidating to the therapist).

4. Your insurance may be invalidated. You should read your policy carefully and check that your public liability extends to covering accidents on clients' property.
5. Compromising/unsafe situations: it is not possible to assess people or circumstances from their first enquiry, which may well be a telephone conversation. You must take every precaution to maintain your personal safety. There have been incidents where therapists have been placed in uncomfortable or even dangerous situations; for example, having been booked over the phone to give treatment to a female only to find, on arrival, a different situation and a man in the house. This leads on to...
6. Loss of control of situation and increased costs (links back to point 3). In a clinic setting you will feel more empowered to deal with a situation and may have other people on the premises. If you are mobile and you decide to take someone with you who helps take your equipment in and maintains a low profile (possibly waiting in the car) this can be quite expensive as they will have to be paid. A male osteopath I know always takes a female 'helper' with him to home visits as a chaperone and a 'witness'. This doubles his salaries bill as he still employs a nurse/receptionist in the clinic to cover his calls etc.
7. Misconception over fees: as the mobile therapist may have fewer overheads, many clients feel the treatment should be cheaper. This is very difficult if you have a treatment room and 'do mobile' as a favour for the less able clients. It is also necessary to cost your travel time into the treatments. If you were based at a clinic you could see a succession of clients in a given time period but, being mobile, you lose out on the number of people you can see in a day.

Mobile therapy practice: advice/discussion

Although there are disadvantages to a mobile practice, many therapists start up this way and have successful visiting practices. Some therapists combine the use of a home room with a mobile practice to increase cost effectiveness and enable the therapist to work outside the home at the noisiest times.

Remember to work out the real costs, such as additional car insurance, petrol and car wear and tear, and work out an average figure for each visit. Then include something for your travel time and add this cost into your treatment charges, otherwise your success will be short-lived as you may be busy but not making a profit.

One point that many mobile therapists have made to me is that when they visit a client's home, the client often has less regard for the therapist's professional time and may ask him/her to wait while the client 'sorts out' a child, or finishes a domestic chore. One extreme example was a client who ordered a take-away meal that arrived during a sport's injury massage and the client expected the therapist to wait while she sat and ate her meal with her partner! It is the therapist's responsibility to make it extremely clear that he/she is leaving at a certain time and the charge will be 'x' amount. The client will then, hopefully, make an effort to focus on the therapy. This also comes back to attitude as mentioned earlier – if you don't respect your time and energy, your client won't.

Points to remember for the mobile therapist are:

- maintain your car; road-worthiness, general checks are extremely important. Your livelihood depends on the reliability of your transport
- don't be tempted to omit the business in your motor insurance. If you need to make a claim, you may find it invalidated if you have not declared business use
- try to book your clients in geographical clusters; thereby saving time and petrol. Keep a mobile phone with you and a list of each day's client contact numbers
- remember your personal safety at all times. If something doesn't feel right, make an excuse and don't enter the property. If, once inside, you find you are uncomfortable, get out as soon as possible and worry about your equipment, oils, remedies, couch etc. afterwards (see 'Meg's Story' *p.46*)
- keep your equipment to a minimum and get a dedicated therapy bag with adequate space for what you need. It will be expensive to start up but will save you numerous trips to the car and make you look less like a 'bag lady/man'.

Renting time (in a clinic, therapy centre or orthodox group practice)

The advantages

1. The legal responsibilities are not the individual therapist's responsibility. Licensing, business rates, planning consent, health and safety are all issues that are someone else's problem.
2. You can choose the times, days, evenings, weekends that best suit your availability and your clients' needs. As you only pay for the sessions you book, you haven't got an unused room at home on a number of days a week, nor are you paying for clinic overheads when it is not being used.
3. If the clinic owner or practice manager is agreeable, you may be able to store things that you need at the clinic. Besides being preferable to transporting everything on a daily basis, having your equipment at your place of work removes unnecessary clutter from your home and will help you run your practice much more smoothly. You may also be able to hang up your diploma/ qualifications and add various decorative touches, such as a soothing picture or a vase of flowers.
4. If the clinic is established, you may well get referrals from other practitioners, which will help build up your practice.
5. Safety: most clinics will have more than one therapist working at any one time, or a receptionist. This alleviates fears for the therapist who may feel vulnerable working one-to-one with no one else around. Even if your session is booked for a time when no one else is usually there, therapists can operate a 'cover' service in which they will stay behind if you have an unknown client and you can do the same for them. Having various therapists around also gives a professional image.

6. If you feel that you are not benefiting your client, you have other therapists that you know, trust and respect within the practice to refer clients on to.
7. Professional image and standards: working from a therapy clinic or multi-disciplinary practice does give a good professional image. In general, it also helps to maintain standards as a certain amount of professional interaction will take place, including discussion covering treatments for certain disorders, articles in journals that you may have otherwise missed, pricing of fees, publicity materials, etc.
8. Costs are likely to be reasonable and you may be able to increase your booked allotted time as your practice increases. Advertising costs such as *Yellow Pages* and newspaper exposure will all be shared. All of this, including your rent, will be tax deductible.
9. There will be some form of contractual agreement. This can be very positive as it can protect you from sudden increases in rent and help you to make short or long term plans about your financial responsibilities, knowing how much you have to pay according to the terms of the contract.
10. Working in a group is preferred by many to working alone at home or independent visiting. The obvious professional advantages of sharing information are also supported by friendship, social communication and a feeling of a distinct professional position among other, similar people.

The disadvantages

1. It is a financial commitment: once you agree to an allotted time – be it weekly, monthly or perhaps bi-monthly to start with – you will have to pay for that amount.
2. You may find it difficult to work with other therapists and prefer to work on your own, or, worse still, encounter personalities within the clinic staff that you clash with.
3. If the clinic is poorly run you may have difficulty accessing messages concerning your appointments.
4. If the clinic manager does not allow storage, this will inhibit your leaving of your therapy necessities and these will have to be transported each time.
5. There may be a clinic corporate clothing image, such as a white tunic with a navy lapel design, that everyone should wear and you may find this unacceptable.
6. You may not wish to join in with advertising/promotional costs, but as one of the therapists you will have to do so or it would be unfair (as clients could ring up enquiring about other therapies but end up becoming your client).

Renting time: advice/discussion

Rental fees usually take one of two forms: either a fixed amount, eg. £40 per day, or a percentage of your appointment income. The percentage will vary from as little as 20% to 55%, usually depending on how much the client desires your services. For example, if it is primarily an osteopathic practice, a second osteopath would be likely to pay 40–50% as they are feasibly taking business from the existing practitioner or possible clinic leaseholder. If, however, you are a remedial masseuse going into this clinic, you are enhancing the clinic's services and very possibly attracting other clients who may be referred to the osteopath. In this instance, the percentage is more likely to be 20–25%.

Both fixed and percentage fees have pros and cons. The most obvious drawback is that you pay the fixed amount whatever, whether you are on holiday or ill. However, the percentage may well seem 'friendlier' but when your practice is thriving you may wish you had gone for the fixed amount as when your takings rise, so does your rent.

Remember, you can't have it all ways. The clinic proprietor still has to pay the bills when the clinic is closed over Christmas etc. Council tax is still paid when you are on holiday too. Occasionally I hear of newly qualified therapists being offered a treatment room 'for free' or for an extremely low rental. I would be very cautious of this, as it is important for you that the clinic is run in a business-like manner. A clinic will have considerable overheads and you should ask how these overheads are met if the therapists are under-charged. Is the clinic meeting all their legal and professional obligations? Is there a catch?

Renting space in a clinic is seen by many as the best compromise. The very fact that there is a financial commitment may help inspire and motivate the therapist. Communication between professionals is always preferable to isolation in terms of practice development and research awareness. In the long term, if you have worked in a multi-disciplinary practice or therapy clinic this will look far better on your CV than working in a spare room at home.

Before you commit, to either a contractual or verbal agreement, ask for a written statement explaining exactly what you will get for your money and what additional charges, such as advertising, there may be. Check if, for example, you can use the phone; whether reception charges are included; whether you are expected to replace anything; are your therapy couch, chairs etc provided? Get a written statement explaining how much rental increase (maximum) can be anticipated and how frequently charges could rise, and check your time for 'get out'. There may be a 12-week commitment period with a necessary 12 weeks' notice. Treatment room hire will increase no more than 15% per annum and will only increase once or twice (by two parts) per annum. This allows everyone to plan financially, but is it fair as the clinic proprietor will have to meet increased utility , rates charges and maintenance? You can also give notice and leave if you find it unacceptable without too heavy a commitment.

Taking on premises (either a lease or buying a suitable business freehold)

The advantages

1. The primary advantage is that you have control over everything: your opening hours; who you sub-let to, if anyone; position and facilities of the building chosen; decor and image.

2. Potential: this is enormous. If you have chosen the right place in the right location, you could have a booming business. You could also cover costs by renting out rooms to other therapists.
3. You can keep your professional life and domestic life separate with no concern about either encroaching on the other.
4. Storage of all professional equipment, remedies, books, journals etc. can all be at the clinic.
5. You can ensure that your professional standards are upheld. You can have strict guidelines as to who could work there, ensuring that less-qualified practitioners do not benefit from your good reputation. You can ensure that all relevant legal responsibilities are covered and that the building has adequate insurance.
6. The cost of the loan, purchase etc. will be tax deductible.
7. If you decide to sell, you may make a profit on the building.

The disadvantages

1. It is a major long-term financial responsibility. In business, things do not always work out as planned.
2. You will most likely need planning permission if there is a 'change of use' of the building, which clearly means that if it is not already a therapy clinic you need to obtain planning consent. If you intend carrying out any structural alterations you will also need planning permission. Laws regarding change of use for the building may apply, as could licensing laws, and you could be held responsible for breaking them. All professional liabilities are down to you.
3. The entire building will be eligible for payment of Capital Gains Tax when you resell (especially considering that you can obtain tax benefits on the payments to purchase).
4. You will be responsible for health and safety and you must take this seriously (see *Chapter 9*).
5. You may be responsible for the maintenance and smooth running of the establishment, from the minor problems such as a toilet that doesn't flush, to a large and expensive roof problem. You should check the lease before commitment, as most leases over 12 months are fully repairing, ie. the incoming tenant has to replace and repair, although some will have a maintenance charge.
6. You may well be judged by the people who work at your clinic, even though they may be self-employed therapists. This necessitates your full trust and respect in their work and performance as otherwise your reputation could be damaged.
7. The security of the clinic is your responsibility. Your insurers may limit the number of keys you give out. You may need an alarm or a metal shutter. Other therapists' equipment may be left on site and, as proprietor, you are ultimately responsible for it.

8. Your life may have an unexpected and major change, eg. an opportunity to work abroad for two years, or an unexpected time demand on your personal life, such as caring for a relative who needs help. Being tied to a long term commitment has a major influence on all other areas of your life. In the early years it may be very difficult to sell without a loss.
9. You must consider the possibility of accident or illness, which sadly has a devastating effect on the self-employed. If your ability to earn is removed, you will not be able to meet those financial demands.

Taking on premises: advice/discussion

Take out insurance to cover loss of earnings in the event of accident or illness. This is another time when honest and accurate accounts are essential. If you have not shown regular earnings, your insurers will not make payment.

You need to have the right attitude to make this kind of venture work: a belief in yourself and a sense of security and inner comfort. Unless you have financial security to start with, you will encounter many stresses and strains, so those who are 'born worriers' or insecure and don't like taking a risk will find it unbearable.

With regard to safety and security, consult a crime prevention officer initially and install all necessary safety and security devices. Have strict clinic procedures. Check stock and keep it as safe as possible (I know of several clinics who have lost numerous books and products due to theft). Money should be kept locked away. Ensure that all therapists and staff are aware of what to do in the event of a fire.

Remember also that a client's property such as jewellery and handbags are the therapist's responsibility during treatment (see 'Codes of conduct', *pp.107–110*). They have every right to expect their safety.

Always keep external doors locked unless you have a receptionist or duty therapist looking after your off-street entrance. It is perfectly acceptable to lock the door and display a sign to the effect: 'The therapist works by appointment only. If the door is locked please telephone'. This is not only for you and your therapist's safety, but also the client's.

This kind of venture can be a very valuable investment. However, it is probably not sensible to embark on an expensive and long-term commitment at the start of your professional practice. Preferably, build up a base level clientele to start with.

Working as self-employed or consultant therapist within the NHS or GP surgery/practice

The advantages

1. Regular income.
2. Reputable work, therefore building up a good reputation for yourself.
3. Working with other health professionals and sharing information.

4. All the benefits of working within a practice, with regular funding and no promotional expenses.
5. Reaching people who need treatments but who could not self-fund.

The disadvantages

1. Few come to mind except that the therapist needs to be extremely clear that they conform to any existing protocols or ward strategies. (An example protocol policy is given under 'Advice/discussion', below).
2. Therapists might encounter prejudice or opposition from orthodox health practitioners working within a more 'biomedical' model.

Working as self-employed or consultant therapist within the NHS or GP surgery/practice: advice/discussion

It is a growing possibility that therapists may be employed to work within hospitals, GP surgeries, rehabilitation clinics and similar orthodox health settings, many of which will be governed by the NHS.

Health authorities and primary care groups now have a clear remit to purchase appropriate and effective healthcare based on the needs of the client group. This enables these purchasers to provide complementary therapists by employing therapists on a sessional basis to provide valuable complementary healthcare resources.

The key questions that healthcare purchasers will consider are:

- the effectiveness of the therapy
- how do they work?
- in what ways do they compare to orthodox treatments?
- how much will a treatment cost, including the cost of the therapist and necessary resources.

We, as therapists, should address the following issues to encourage wide employment of complementary therapists within the NHS:

- provision of data that ensures credibility and effectiveness of complementary therapists. Research should include clinical trials
- encourage regulatory control of complementary therapies. Try to take an active role in national registration, databases and an 'umbrella' body for each therapy
- assessment of need and demand for complementary therapies. How much more work would there be if clients do not have to pay directly for their treatment
- purchasers who already use a complementary therapist's services can be networked to encourage new prospective complementary therapy budgets.

An example of the above is the East London and the City Health Authority. ELCHA has funded the Royal London Homeopathic Hospital and many other contracts exist within this health authority, including 'Bodywise' in Bethnal

Green. Homeopathy, osteopathy and acupuncture are currently funded in this way in Birmingham. The European Social Fund has been diverted to employ complementary therapists for inner city pre-natal and mother and baby groups where aromatherapists, an active birth teacher and reflexologist work alongside midwives and health visitors. Self-employed therapists submit invoices for their services and the service manager processes funding.

Various people can be contacted to discuss the possibility of purchasing your services, eg. family health services authority, local GP fund holders, hospitals, hospices, clinics and practice managers.

In so far as supplying remedies, as opposed to skills is concerned, there are cases of cost effectiveness. Herbal preparations may be cheaper than synthetic drugs, for example 'Crataegus' compares with ACE inhibitors for heart failure, 'Hypericum' compares favourably with selective serotonin uptake inhibitors in depression. These two remedies have proven effectiveness (Weihmayr and Ernst, 1995). For further information on efficacy see *Chapter 1*.

If you are invited to be a therapist or consultant therapist at a hospital or hospice where a protocol does not exist, get one in place for everyone's protection, including your own.

A sample hospital protocol (based on design by Buckle, 1997)

* Consent (written) from the patient, the patient's hospital consultant, support nursing staff and hospital administration.

* Qualifications: write into the policy minimum standards of qualifications for therapists working within the area as the issue of cascade training within hospital settings has serious repercussions. In cascade training one qualified therapist shows many other health assistants and carers certain techniques, such as a few reflex points, one or two shiatsu stretches, a brief hand massage. The unqualified carer then administers the therapy to the people within his/her care. This is an abuse of care if the person is not trained to recognise danger signs or make professional judgements, and it is also unlikely that they would be insured to practise. Should problems arise, the health authority may find themselves on dangerous ground. Training documentation should be kept on the ward/work area.

* Health and safety: safety guides concerning the therapy should be kept to hand, eg. guides for disposal of needles for acupuncture, storage of essential oils for aromatherapists etc. COSHH assessments should be documented for each treatment.

* Reference books with information about the therapy should be stored in a convenient place.

* All/any legislation concerning the therapy should be documented with clear guidelines, easily accessible and always adhered to.

* Storage: remedies, oils and herbs must be safely stored in their correct environment, locked with keys kept only by qualified therapists or senior, responsible staff.

* Lengths of treatment: given a maximum length of time any patient should receive treatment, and over a given period of time and frequency. Remember many patients in a hospital or hospice will be more vulnerable and less sturdy than the average client at large. An example of record keeping here might be:

Mr Smith: Reflexology treatment   Consultant _____

Maximum time, 50 minutes no more than every third day

To continue for 15 days only (maximum)

Commencing date _____

(Keep with consent and treatment records)

* Suppliers: therapeutic remedies, essential oils, homeopathic remedies etc. These must be reputable. The therapist may use their own (and take responsibility). If the ward is to provide these, great diligence must be taken to investigate what is 'good' and that suppliers can validate their product, whether it is a botanical species, herb or essential oil. Documentation of supplies, batch number, use-by dates should be recorded with treatment records.

* Record keeping: each client should have extensive and accurate record notes kept of each treatment with all relevant data including treatment/changes in treatment.

* Location of treatments: if at all possible, therapy treatments should be given in a designated area, preferably a treatment room just for therapy. The busy ward area with noise and lack of privacy is not the best environment. Many hospitals now have special rooms. The University Hospital, Birmingham, has several special complementary therapy interest groups. One specialist oncology ward got the television show *Real Rooms* to decorate and refurbish their therapy room. It was then featured on the programme in the 1998 series.

* Always maintain the privacy and wishes of the client/patient. Because of the nature of a hospital environment, there is sometimes a feeling of being 'public'. This should not be so with a holistic/complementary therapist. Always consider what is the best circumstance possible for the client and treatment you are going to give, and maintain those optimum conditions each time.

After these points of protocol, a list of therapist's responsibilities could be distributed, for example:

- accountable practitioners are responsible for maintaining and updating their skills, knowledge and professional development
- practitioners must ensure adequate professional supervision (particularly relevant to counselling and psychotherapy)
- each member of the team must accept certain responsibilities, eg. qualifications and competence standards must be recorded by management/ hospital staff and checked that only those therapists or staff who have reached these standards offer the treatment to patients
- unit manager must ensure that appropriate insurance covers relevant practice (either within organisation structure or through individual practitioners)
- each therapist is totally responsible for maintaining treatment records for each patient
- professional accountability is of major importance: always protect the interests of the client.

All in all, for many complementary therapy practitioners, the opportunity to work within such an environment is a privilege and an excellent way of earning a regular income while developing good clinical skills and working within a team of health practitioners. The fact that it may mean a more structured approach than the therapist is used to is not necessarily a bad thing as it develops other skills and encourages a greater awareness of health and safety and accountability issues.

Conclusion

As mentioned earlier, it is possible to get work in complementary therapies in a multitude of different environments. It would be beyond the scope of this book to consider every single possibility. The usual options have been covered, and most other areas – such as working as an aromatherapist in a health spa or leisure club – are frequently arranged by employment rather than self-employment or own business. (Working on a sessional basis for health spas is often quite badly paid in comparison to self-employment.)

Inevitably the complementary therapist has to make choices and decisions that are appropriate and beneficial to themselves. Initial budget, earning potential, long term plans, attitude to risk and responsibility will all have a bearing on the venue you choose.

Exercises

1. Consider the advantages versus the disadvantages of working in your own home.

2. Look around for suitable premises, make enquiries about rental costs, lease and freehold prices.
3. Write to possible venues such as residential care homes to see if they might offer you any work and provide a room.

References

Birmingham City Council (1996) *Home based work activity*. Department of Planning and Architecture, Birmingham

Birmingham City Council (1990) *Application for Licensing and The Licensing Act*. Available from the Department of Environmental Services, Licensing Section, Birmingham

Buckle J (1997) *Clinical Aromatherapy in Nursing*. Arnold, London: 103–108

Hereford Council (1982) *Licensing Application*. Department of Environmental Health and Trading Standards, available from Hereford Council

HSBC (1998) *Working from Home Business Fact Sheet*. Available from HSBC Bank

Weihmayr T, Ernst E (1995) Quoted in Ernst E (1996) *Complementary Medicine – An Objective Appraisal*. Butterworth Heinneman, London

A real life incident experience by Meg Harvey, an aromatherapist

I made an appointment for a lady's massage in her own home. On arrival I went to the living room and set up as per normal procedure. Ten minutes or so into the massage a man walked in dressed in shorts and sat on the sofa. I waited for him to speak or turn the television on or something, but he just sat there – he didn't pick a book up, didn't speak, did nothing. Odd, I thought, but chose to ignore it.

Another ten minutes later, another man walked in, sat down and did the same thing. Right, I thought, I now feel uncomfortable and unsafe. I told the lady I was stopping the massage and would she get off the table please. She got off the table, sat down, never asked why or made any comment at all, which actually reassured me I was not over-reacting. Nobody said or did anything. I packed up and left in silence.

6

Legal aspects

Your first decision concerns the legal form under which your business will operate, ie. sole trader, partnership, limited company or worker co-operative. You will be influenced in the choice you make by the financial needs of the business, consideration of personal liability and the degree of personal control that you may wish to seek. There are many professionals, such as solicitors, accountants, bankers, insurance brokers, business consultants and small firm advisors, who can provide the basic information to ensure that your business is established on the right footing. You would be well advised to contact a professional advisor once you have given some thought to the following choices.

A **sole trader** is an individual operating independently. As a sole trader you take personal responsibility for the debts of your business and should meet these from your personal wealth if your business fails. The profits from the business, less any personal allowances etc., will be subject to income tax. However, it is a very simple form of business organisation that is commonly found in trades where small amounts of finance are required. Many people prefer to work for themselves and become self-employed because they like the idea of being independent. The advantages of this kind of business are:

- freedom and flexibility
- personal satisfaction
- enjoyment of profits
- personal control with no requirement to consult others
- absence of legal formalities when establishing the business.

The disadvantages or drawbacks of sole trading are:

- full personal responsibility for decisions and for the debts of the business
- success depends on the owner's energy and fitness
- no continuity of existence, since the business dies with the owner
- the responsibility for a range of separate tasks rests on the shoulders of the owner, eg. paperwork, tax returns
- dealing with suppliers as well as customers
- unlimited liability, ie. in the event of bankruptcy they will lose not only the organisation as such, but could also lose other assets including their home.

The sole trader can run a business under the individual's name; however, if another name is to be used, the individual's name must still appear somewhere on all business stationery, the rationale being that creditors should know with whom they are conducting business.

A **partnership** is similar to sole trader status except that it involves more than one person. A sole trader will often take on a partner when there is too much work to be done, or when extra skills are required. The partners are liable for the debts of the business and the profits of the business are subject to income tax. This type of set-up needs long and careful discussion between the partners involved and it is wise to 'brainstorm' all possible eventualities that may affect the business so that agreements can be drawn up between partners. Partners should be chosen very carefully since every partner, when acting on behalf of the business, acts as an agent of the partnership and can thus bind their fellow partners. Following on from this, an individual partner can be sued personally and held liable for all decisions made, and debts incurred, by other partners.

As with the sole trader, it is possible to set up a partnership without any legal formalities. However, one should consider entering into a legal contract called a 'Deed of Partnership' which sets out the rights and responsibilities of each partner. This document should also allow for the continuation of the business in the event of the death or retirement of one of the partners.

A **limited liability company** is a more complex arrangement. Particular documents must be deposited with the Register of Companies and you will need to consult an accountant, auditor or solicitor concerning these. A limited company is a separate entity in law, and the company, rather than you personally, is liable for its debts. The owners of limited companies are called shareholders because they each own a part of the business. Shareholders enjoy the privilege of limited liability, which means that they are liable to meet the debts of the company only to the extent that they have invested in the business. One of the major disadvantages of the private limited company is that it is more restrictive and formal in nature. It must publish annual accounts and file annual returns giving details of the directors, shareholders and other information required by law.

A **co-operative** is simply a business enterprise which is owned and controlled by all those working in it. Everyone has an equal share in making decisions about how the business is run, plus an equal share of the profits. At least two people are required to form a co-operative.

Registration of a business name

All that any business is legally bound to do is to display all directors' names and addresses at which notices may be served on all business stationery and at business premises, and be prepared to produce this information when requested by customers and suppliers. A leaflet entitled *Disclosure Requirements* is obtainable from Companies House (see *Appendix I,* 'Useful addresses').

Special legal aspects

Complementary therapists work in the public service arena, offering treatments that purport to improve or maintain the health and well being of the client. There are general aspects of legal obligation, but individual therapies may have their own legislation and some local authority by-laws will vary geographically.

Many authorities have a Licensing Act that applies to massage therapists, sports injury therapists, aromatherapists etc. There is a great imbalance as to whether or not practitioners have to pay a licence fee to become licensed or whether they are exempt. There is also a large discrepancy in the nature of the licensing and the amount of form filling any one therapist is subjected to. As an example, the Birmingham City Council Act 1990 states that it is 'An Act to authorise the control of establishments for massage or special treatment in the city of Birmingham' [28.9.90]. The bias of this Act could be seen to be very subjective and derisive to therapists, emphasising the seedy side of massage establishments with saunas and informing the police constabulary of the establishment and the licence application.

The licensing acts could, in fact, be useful legislation to orthodox practitioners as the Act could help maintain the reputation of the integrity of the profession as:

Section 4 from the Act

(1) On considering an application for a licence or the renewal of a licence under this Act the Council shall take into consideration any representations which may be made to the Council by the chief constable with respect to the application or the establishment to which it relates.

(2) The Council may refuse to grant or renew a licence under this Act or may revoke a licence so granted in the case of –

a) any person under the age of 21

b) any person who has been convicted of an offence under the Sexual Offences Acts 1956 to 1976 or the Street Offences Act 1959 or who may be otherwise unsuitable to hold such a licence

c) any premises which are unsuitable for the purposes of an establishment for massage or special treatment or in which the accommodation or provision for such treatment is not reasonably adequate or suitable

d) any establishment which has been or is being improperly conducted

e) any establishment in which adequate professional, technical or other staff is not available for the administration of such massage or special treatment as may there be provided; or

f) any establishment which is being carried on in contravention of the provisions of the Act or any by-law made thereunder.

(Birmingham City Council Act, 1990)

For reputable practitioners this kind of regulation is not necessarily a bad thing, but the 'bias' in which it can be presented may be offensive. It must be remembered though, that further sections of the act make a statement that if you do offer massage without obtaining the correct license you are breaking the law:

Section 3 (1) As from the commencement of this Act, no person shall carry on an establishment for massage or special treatment in the city without a licence from the Council authorising him to do so.

(Birmingham City Council Act, 1990)

This clearly means that if you use massage in your therapy you need a licence. It is therefore imperative to check with your local council, usually the Environmental Services Department, Licensing Section. The annual cost will vary and will increase if you offer more than one type of treatment. It is currently hundreds of pounds per year; the more sceptical could think it is just another form of indirect tax.

As the questions and form filling vary as these two examples below show the attitude and amount of information neede by councils, varies substantially.

Birmingham City	**Herefordshire Council**
Five A4 pages	One A4 page with simple questions
13(a) Does the applicant propose to carry on a visiting massage service? Either from the licensed premises or elsewhere?	Are you or have you ever been registered by any local authority in connection with massage activities? (If so, give details.)

19 Give details of the times during which it is proposed that the premises shall be open:
  i) days of the week
  ii) hours of the day
	Have you or any member of your staff ever been convicted of any offence in connection with such activities? (If so, give details.)
	Specify any relevant qualifications that you or your staff possess.

Exemption to the Licensing Acts

The Birmingham City Council Act has several exemptions that may be worth exploring (see below). Other councils have similar exemptions that may be of interest if you are setting up a practice within a nursing home or similar establishment.

The act does not apply to:

Section 9   (1)   a) An establishment for massage or special treatment carried on by a registered medical practitioner or by a member of any organisation or association which specifies qualifications by way of training for and experience of the therapy concerned for the practice by its members of chiropractic, osteopathy, naturopathy or acupuncture, being a member who is required by that organisation or association to observe professional standards in such practice; or

b) any hospital provided by the Secretary of State or by a charity which is registered under section 4 of the Charities Act 1960 or which, by virtue of subsection (4) of that section is not required to be registered or

(c) any nursing home which is for the time being registered under Part II of the Registered Homes Act 1984 or exempted from registration under that Part; or

d) any premises which are an establishment for massage or special treatment merely by reason of face or scalp massage being administered in those premises.

(2)   Subsection (1) of section 3 (licensing of persons to carry on establishments) of this Act shall not apply to a person registered by any board established under the Professions Supplementary to Medicine Act 1960, a member of the Chartered Society of Physiotherapy who is not so registered or to a registered nurse.

(3)   Nothing in this Act shall prejudice or affect the operation of any of the relevant statutory provisions as defined in Part 1 of the Health and Safety at Work Act 1974.

The above exemptions are an insult to many massage therapists who belong to extremely reputable, professional organisations with codes of practice and ethics. The act suggests that they might not be considered as reputable or professional as a nurse or physiotherapist who carries out massage, although not actually trained in massage therapy.

An equally provoking anomaly is the difference between one council and another. For example, many of the London boroughs have exempted aromatherapists who belong to the Register of Qualified Aromatherapists (RQA). The RQA campaigned over a long period of time on behalf of their membership to exempt them from the licensing laws imposed by Birmingham City Council. Their efforts were sadly unsuccessful. Therapists may have trained at the same training establishment but by working in different areas they will be liable to different local legislation and fees.

It should be emphasised that if it is local legislation you should comply. If you have not and you advertise your therapy, it is likely that the Licensing Officer in your area will find out and you will have to comply as well as be liable for arrears.

The Consumer Protection Act 1987 is also relevant to complementary therapists who sell on anything that may possibly have an area of safety concern to the public. As with safety regulations, you may be found to have committed an offence, even when nobody has been injured.

Contravention of the 'General Safety Requirement' can lead to a fine of £2,000, up to six months in prison or both. The general safety requirement (Section 10 of the Consumer Protection Act 1987) refers to goods being reasonably safe, having regard to all the circumstances. For example, aromatherapists who sell essential oils should be extremely particular over clear labelling, information, dilution advice, promotional material and integral single drop dispensers. This one factor of integral dispensers has been flagged as the precaution that has the greatest influence on children's safety.

Therapeutic claims made by aromatherapists or herbalists are another tricky legal area.

The key legal provisions are found in regulations 2, 4 and 9 of the Advertising Regulations Section 12 (1):

> Advertisements and labels/leaflets may be issued. Advertisements must comply with Regulations 2 and 4. Regulation 2 prohibits advertisements which are likely to lead to the use of medicinal products or other substances or articles for the purpose of treatment or diagnosis of specific named diseases – venereal diseases, cancer, diabetes, tuberculosis, epilepsy, kidney disease, paralysis, cataracts or glaucoma. Regulation 4 prohibits advertisements (including labels and leaflets) likely to lead to the use of the product for the purpose of the treatment of various diseases set out in Schedule 2 (subject to exceptions). Under regulation 4(1) advertisements may be issued for the treatment of eczema, but not for arthritis (save for the purpose of symptomatic relief of muscular pain and stiffness – see Part III of Schedule 2).

Information from the Medicine Control Agency,
Department of Health, May 1999

There have been regular threats to herbal remedies, essential oils, nutritional supplements and many other 'alternative remedies' about making them less available or licensed medical products sourced through pharmacies only, which may affect cost and availability. The Medicines Control Agency (MCA), Department of Health has for some time been comparing EC directives that relate to 'medicinal products' with respect to whether a product is a medicine or not. Herbal remedies are currently covered by exemption terms (Section 12) from medicinal licensing, as not being 'relevant medicinal products':

Section 12   (1)   The restrictions imposed by sections 7 or 8 of the Act (ie. the requirement for licences) do not apply to the sale, supply, manufacture or assembly of any herbal remedy in the course of a business where –

a) the remedy is manufactured or assembled on premises of which the person carrying on the business is the occupier and which he is able to close so as to exclude the public, and the person carrying on the business sells or supplies the remedy for administration to a particular person after being requested by or on behalf of that person and in that person's presence to use his own judgement as to the treatment required.

The position of aromatherapy products is still a little unclear, but it would seem to be in the interest of the public and aromatherapy for these products to remain exempt. In the summer of 1999 the government was still reviewing lists of exemptions.

In July 1999 the Department of Health announced proposals to make the MCA's classification procedure more open, transparent, consistent and credible with regulations intended later in that year. We are assured that 'there is nothing in the proposals which affect the status of food supplements and herbal remedies. The government is committed to ensuring that consumer choice and the availability of health products are not restricted' (Baroness Hayman Press Release, Department of Health, 15 July 1999).

On-going legislation and reform inevitably affect us all.

Professional codes of conduct and ethics

The very nature of working within a professional framework means that we, as complementary therapists, agree by virtue of the membership to comply with certain codes.

Examples are given in *Appendices II* and *III* of some of the codes from the BCMA and specifically the Codes of Conduct of the IFA.

It is relevant to consider our working codes and ethics with legal aspects as:

1. Law and ethics are both instruments of regulation, dictating how people should behave.
2. They are instruments used to determine good practice.
3. Ethics within professional codes of practice encourage optimum standards of behaviour.
4. Law is about enforcing minimum standards.
5. Ethical decisions are usually the best result that can be reached at the end of a detailed and fair process that has taken all possible considerations into account.
6. Usually (but not always) what is ethical is legal.

Legal controls

The effect of the lack of regulation of many complementary therapies combined with their enormous growth in popularity could lead to a potentially dangerous state of affairs. There is a high level of voluntary self-regulation and active professional associations, many of which have membership criteria, helping to protect the public. However, it could be thought that further regulation is necessary to safeguard the public, eg. compulsory national registration for each therapy, a protection of title and statutory practice premises requirements.

Where greater regulation is in place, there is a more structured accountability. Accountability is vital in circumstances where a client has a case against a practitioner for unacceptable professional conduct, professional incompetence or general suitability to practise. An example of this legal control is within the osteopathic profession. The General Council of Registered Osteopaths (GCRO) has a referral system via an investigating committee, to the professional conduct committee or the health committee, as appropriate.

> *Where the Professional Misconduct Committee makes an adverse finding against the practitioner, it has a variety of penalties at its disposal – it may admonish the osteopath, suspend registration, impose conditions on registration, or erase the practitioner from the register.*

(Stone and Matthews, 1996)

Although it would be outside the scope of this book to discuss at length actions in law, there are various types of action that a client may decide to bring against a practitioner according to Stone and Matthews (1996). These include:

* Negligence: the client must prove that the practitioner owed the client 'a duty of care', that the practitioner was in breach of that duty and that, as a result, the client suffered harm.

* Battery: common law recognises that every person has the right to have 'his body integrity' respected. If practitioners touch patients in any way when they have no authority to do so they lay themselves open to a potential battery action.

* Failure to warn: most cases of failure to warn are brought in actions of negligence. When a practitioner fails to disclose material risks involved in the therapy, they are risking this legal action as the disclosure may have affected the client's agreement to accept a treatment.

The above emphasises the importance of **consent** and **information**, combining to **informed consent**. A therapist must never dispense with consent. Also, 'it is highly advisable that practitioners write down any warnings given to their patients' (Stone and Matthews, 1996).

Julia Stone also advises us that a consent form is not a *carte blanche* form for treatment.

Criminal law

All therapists are of course subject to criminal law. Prosecutions have been brought against healthcare professionals in criminal areas. Logically, therapists could face similar charges. For example:

* Manslaughter: in a situation where the practitioner's conduct has been so inadequate that it could attract criminal liability, when a client has died.

* Duties toward children: parents and guardians have a duty to provide medical aid for children under 16 (Children's Act, 1989). If a parent insists on his or her child receiving complementary therapy when orthodox treatment would be more beneficial, and where the child has suffered as a result, the practitioner who treated the child could be charged with aiding and abetting the parent in his or her breach of duty.
* Misrepresentation: (Misrepresentation Act, 1967) where a client has been 'induced' to receive treatment and suffers harm as a result, or where a bogus practitioner has lied about the efficacy or validity of the treatment; if the patient consequently suffers and misrepresentation can be proved, the therapist could be prosecuted. In this instance, a practitioner could also be prosecuted under the Fair Trading Act (1983).

The scenario is not as worrying as it may appear. According to Stone (1996) cases brought against orthodox practitioners are escalating, while there is no evidence to suggest that there is any increase in cases brought against complementary practitioners. Several reasons could be suggested, such as that there may be difficulty establishing that a therapist has caused harm or possibly some cases are settled out of court. Whatever the situation, it is essential that practitioners are held accountable when they have been negligent, fraudulent, caused harm or breached any codes of conduct. This also underpins the responsibility of every practitioner to have professional insurance (see *Chapter 7*).

Exercises

1. Look up your profession's codes of practice and read them.
2. Telephone the local council's environmental services section for licensing and enquire about licensing in your area. Make sure that you are practising legally.
3. Review all of your promotional material and ensure that you are not making any beneficial claims which may be incorrect, dubious or, at worst, illegal.

Relevant draft unit from National Occupational Standards (NOS)

C2 Determine the legal and financial requirements for setting up and operating the business

The elements of competence:

C2.1 Define the requirements of the ownership and the trading status of the business

C2.2 Determine the means by which the business will be set up and funded

C2.3 Identify the controls needed for the legal and financial operation of the business.

The above unit requires the therapist to:

- investigate options for ownership of the business and the implications of each option
- investigate funding options and business controls for effective operation
- decide on appropriate status and funding for the business.

This unit is aimed at anyone who has to identify legal and financial factors involved in the setting up and operation of a small business (NOS, 1997). This unit is also relevant for *Chapter 4*.

References

Birmingham City Council (1990) *Birmingham City Council Licensing Act*: Chapter xiii

Birmingham Venture (1990) *Starting a Business in Birmingham*. Birmingham Chamber of Commerce Publication

British Complementary Medicine Association (1987) *Code of Conduct* (see *Appendix I*, 'Useful addresses')

The Consumer Protection Act (1987) HMSO, London. Publisher, Location

Disclosure Requirements. Companies House (see *Appendix I*, 'Useful addresses')

Department of Health Press Release: *Baroness Hayman Announces Changes in Proposals on Borderline Products Classification Process*: 15th July 1999

Herefordshire Council (1998) *Application for Registration of Premises and Persons Carrying on the Practice of Massage*

International Federation of Aromatherapists (1986) *Code of Ethics*. IFA , London: October

International Federation of Aromatherapists (1989) *Code of Conduct*. IFA, London: August

National Occupational Standards (NOS) (1997) *Consultation Pack, Section B, Setting up Practice Units. Written for the Care Sector Consortium.* Prime Research and Development Ltd, Harrogate

Stone J, Matthews J (1996) *Complementary Medicine and the Law.* Oxford University Press, New York: 139–192

Woodfield R (1999) *Regulatory Position of Aromatherapy Products.* Statement to the Aromatherapy Trade Council on behalf of the Medicines Control Agency (MCA). DOH, London

7

Insurance

One of the most important considerations of any business is insurance. You should not view insurance as an unnecessary overhead – it could be the difference between going out of business or staying in business, if the worst happens. There are various types of insurance that a complementary therapist needs to think about. The following provides you with a summary of the more important classes of insurance available.

'Professional liability' insurance

This cover is **vital**, and it would be very imprudent to start practising without it. Any person who provides a service, advice or goods in a professional capacity owes a duty of care to clients and other third parties. As a professional, you will be seen by your clients as someone who knows their subject thoroughly, and in these days of high consumer awareness they are more likely than ever to take legal action against you if they consider that you have been negligent, or even if they feel that you have provided a sub-standard service. We now live in a very litigious age and the number of claims being made has risen sharply in recent years, as has the size of the court awards.

You may feel that the claim is unfounded, and stands little chance of success, which may be the case, but it will need defending and legal defence costs can run into thousands of pounds.

One claim against you for alleged negligence could put you out of business, or even worse, cause financial ruin unless you hold suitable insurance. This will provide legal defence costs and cover any court award if the claimant is successful.

The types of policy available carry various names including: 'Professional indemnity', 'Malpractice', 'Professional liability' and 'Public liability with "Treatment" cover', which can be confusing for the therapist. In practice, policies generally fall into two categories:

1. Public liability

This type of cover tends to be widely available, mainly as it is the preferred basis for most of the larger insurance companies who underwrite insurance for complementary therapists. The cover provided by this policy can be broken down into four main elements:
* Legal liability for injury to clients or other third parties not involving treatment or advice. 'Trip 'n slip' cover, in other words.

* Legal liability for loss or damage to property belonging to clients and other third parties.

* Legal liability for injury to third parties or damage to their property caused by a defect in a product that you have sold or supplied. The European Products Liability laws are very onerous and anyone in the chain of supply is potentially liable, whether they manufacture the product themselves or buy in to sell on.

* Legal liability arising out of any treatment administered or advice given.

It is the 'treatment' cover that needs looking at the most closely to ensure that you have adequate cover for your particular vocation, as the cover on offer from various insurers can differ. Some policy wordings only provide cover where there has been actual bodily injury or damage, whereas others are on a 'breach of professional duty' basis, which would cover claims not involving treatment or advice given. Examples of this type of claim include:

* A client takes legal action against you as he or she lost his or her job because of an alleged breach of confidentiality on your part.

* You are sued for alleged libel or slander. This is particularly important if you are likely to write articles for journals or magazines, or take part in radio or TV broadcasts.

* You are asked by a client to provide a report (for a fee). The client subsequently alleges that they suffered financial loss as a result of an error or omission in your report, and takes legal action against you.

If you are offered cover on a 'public liability plus treatment' basis, and you are unsure about the extent of cover, ask your insurance broker or insurance company to confirm in writing whether the above types of claim would be covered. If you arrange your insurance through a professional body which you are a member of, do not just accept verbal assurance from the professional body – insist that they obtain confirmation in writing from the insurance broker or company!

2. Professional indemnity

This type of cover tends to be the favoured basis of Lloyds of London and some smaller insurance companies. In simple terms, the 'professional indemnity' cover replaces the 'treatment/advice' element of cover found under public liability policies, as described above. A good professional indemnity wording would automatically incorporate breach of confidentiality, libel and slander, consultancy work etc. Treatment or advice do not need to be involved – the question is: 'Has the client or other third party suffered financial loss as a result of your alleged neglect, error or omission?'

Any professional indemnity policy must, of course, be extended to include 'general' public liability and products liability cover as explained above.

Other issues, which may be relevant depending on your circumstances, include:

* Does the policy cover teaching and tuition risks as well as the 'practising' risk? If not, will the insurer charge extra to include these?

* Are you covered for any work carried out before you effected cover? Claims often arise several months after the actual provision of services.

* Similarly, if you stop practising and cancel the policy, would cover apply if a claim arose after the cancellation for services provided during the currency of the policy?

* Does the policy cover good samaritan acts, voluntary work or first aid treatment?

* Are you covered for work performed outside the UK or for products sold to persons living abroad?

* What is the indemnity limit under the policy? A minimum of £1,000,000 would be prudent.

Clearly, your aim should be to secure as wide a cover as possible, although the level of premium may be a more important factor to you. If you obtain your insurance via a group scheme run by an association of which you are a member you will not have any choice as to the extent of cover, so it is important to ensure, as best you can, that this is adequate for your own personal requirements. If you have any doubts you should contact an insurance broker who specialises in arranging cover for complementary therapists and ask for their help.

Employers' liability insurance

If you employ anybody, you need to effect cover by law in case the employee is injured, becomes ill or dies while in your employment. Under the Employers' Liability Act, the definition of 'employee' is very wide, and includes casual employees, self-employed persons and persons working under Youth Opportunity schemes. Employers' liability insurance protects against an employee or their personal representatives making a claim of alleged negligence as an employer, and would provide legal defence costs as well as cover any court award. Nowadays, most insurers automatically provide a minimum indemnity of £10,000,000.

Personal accident and sickness insurance

If you are unable to work because of an accident or illness, your income is likely to dry up. Unless you have some other means of support, such as a spouse or a partner earning enough money to support both of you, or substantial savings, you should consider effecting private cover. Do not rely on state benefits, which are inadequate as well as being complicated and time-consuming to obtain.

This cover is particularly important if you do not have any other source of income and have monthly commitments such as mortgage or rent payments, HP payments or utility bills – not to mention every day living expenses like food and clothing.

Cover can be arranged for 'personal accident' only, which tends to be relatively inexpensive, or for personal accident and sickness, which can be expensive depending on the weekly benefit required. Typically, insurance companies will provide cover for up to two thirds of your normal weekly income. The reason they will not provide 100% of your income is partly because of the state benefits available, but also because they want to encourage you to return to work. As well as a weekly benefit, many policies also offer 'lump sums' for more serious injuries resulting in loss of eyes, limbs, permanent disablement or accidental death. Personal accident policies generally provide world-wide cover; those policies that provide the illness cover as well tend to be more restricted, but do provide cover in Europe and the western world, plus other countries such as Australia, New Zealand and Japan. Generally speaking, those countries with poor medical facilities, such as certain tropical countries with ongoing civil unrest, would be excluded.

Personal accident/sickness policies typically pay out for up to two years, and then the weekly benefit would cease. If cover is required for longer than this, it is possible to effect 'permanent health' cover (otherwise known as 'income protection'), which can provide cover up to retirement if required. As you might expect, the premiums for this type of cover are more expensive, although it is possible to bring them down by excluding, say, the first four weeks or perhaps 13 weeks of disability.

Another form of disability cover is 'critical illness' insurance. This type of policy pays out a lump sum, as opposed to a regular income, should you be diagnosed as suffering from one of the conditions covered by the policy, or become permanently and totally disabled following an illness or accident.

For advice on permanent health insurance or critical illness cover you should contact an independent financial adviser.

Business equipment and stock

If you set up a healing centre, the cost of fitting out can be substantial. As well as massage tables and other equipment directly related to your particular discipline, you are likely to have some or all of the following: computers, fax machine, telephone, copier, stereo equipment, desk/s, chair/s, carpets, curtains etc.

Many insurers offer 'surgery combined' policies, which are primarily aimed at doctors' surgeries, but they are also suitable for healing centres. They would provide loss or damage cover on all contents, plus money, business interruption (following fire etc.), glass/sanitary-ware breakage, employers' liability and public liability.

Even if you start up in business in a more modest fashion by working from home, as the majority of therapists would do, you would still be advised to consider effecting insurance to avoid any financial hardship should you be unfortunate enough to lose or damage equipment or stock. Make sure that any policy you arrange provides cover wherever you might be working in the UK, including at clients' houses and while you were transporting equipment in your car. You might not think that a massage table is a particularly attractive target for a thief, but the writer has dealt with several claims for thefts from unattended vehicles.

Incidentally, do not assume that your home contents policy covers such items. Indeed, it is very unlikely that cover does apply unless your insurer offers a 'business equipment extension' under their policy.

On the question of household insurance, if you work from home you should tell your insurers and ask them to confirm in writing that they have noted this. If you do not, then you may find out that cover is invalidated and your insurers will not pay out, even if the claim is nothing to do with your complementary therapy business. Some insurers do not allow businesses to be run from home under any circumstances, and if this is the case, you will have to switch to a more tolerant insurer. Even those insurers who will provide cover for policyholders working from home are likely to endorse the policy to exclude:

- claims under the public liability section of the policy arising out of your occupation
- theft of contents or other personal effects not involving forcible entry to the house. In other words, theft by a client lawfully in your house would not be covered.

Pension planning

Unless you have pension provision from another occupation or you consider that your spouse/partner will provide for you in retirement, you should consider making provision for your retirement. Under current legislation, you will receive a State pension, but this is unlikely to be adequate; at best, a State pension is only likely to provide a very basic income. There are various savings vehicles that can be utilised to provide income in retirement, but the most popular way of doing this is to effect a 'personal pension' policy.

Insurance companies and other pension providers will allow you to start a plan paying a regular monthly contribution, or investing a lump sum. The minimum monthly contributions vary between insurers and other pension providers, but some companies will accept as little as £25.00 per month.

The Government has recently announced that 'stakeholder' pensions will be introduced in April 2001 if everything goes according to plan. While final details are not known at the time of going to press, the basic premise of stakeholder pensions is that they will have lower charges, no penalties for stopping contributions or transferring the fund to another provider, and they will be secure. Most insurance companies will be offering this type of pension plan.

For advice on stakeholder pensions and pensions generally, you should contact an independent financial adviser.

The ideal position would be to effect all of the aforementioned policies, although it is appreciated that the cost is likely to be prohibitive, particularly in the early stages of your business. This being the case, you will have to prioritise according to your own requirements, with professional liability cover being your first choice.

One final word: do not always choose a policy on price alone. Insurance is like any commodity – generally speaking, you get what you pay for.

Exercises

1. Check your buildings and contents insurance for any business exclusions.
2. If you already have professional insurance, read through the policy and check that you are covered for all aspects of your therapy practice.
3. If you wish to work abroad, ensure that your insurance covers you outside of the UK; also check for what period of time.
4. Contact different companies who provide personal accident and sickness insurance and compare costs and benefits.

Source

All information on insurance is contributed by Stephen Watling of Ecology Insurance Brokers (see *Appendix I,* 'Useful addresses')

8

Marketing

Marketing is one of the most important aspects of setting up your business yet is often disregarded as being too difficult to understand or too expensive: it is neither of these. Marketing is applied common sense. Put simply, it is finding out who your clients are, what they want and delivering it in a way that is appealing to them. At the same time, you have to set prices that are attractive to your clients while still allowing you a good profit margin. Finally, you have to make sure potential clients are aware of what you have to offer through promotion. These are the four Ps of marketing: product, place, price and promotion.

This chapter is divided into three key stages (think, plan, act), taking you logically through the marketing process. It provides a practical guide to marketing, demonstrating that by taking a planned approach you can fulfil your objectives cost effectively.

Think

SWOT analysis

This is a basic marketing tool that makes you think about your business, your **S**trengths, **W**eaknesses, **O**pportunities and **T**hreats. Use the following template to set out your own strengths (what do you have on your side?), weaknesses (what don't you do well?), opportunities (where can you assert yourself?) and threats (where are you vulnerable?). The SWOT layout puts positive aspects on the left and negative ones on the right. It is important to be honest with yourself.

Do not restrict yourself to a single sheet of paper: you may wish to use one sheet, or more, for each category.

You should then analyse what you have written, recognising that each strength must have a corresponding weakness, opportunity and threat. For example,

Strength	=	good verbal communication skills.
Weakness	=	may sometimes talk too much.
Opportunity	=	use situations where verbal dexterity is important.
Threat	=	avoid situations where confidentiality is crucial.

Opportunity implies movement, going towards an aim. As we move towards the aim we might be vulnerable to new threats from directions we have not been focusing on up to now. Therefore, every opportunity will have a corresponding threat, which needs to be added to the list.

Consequently, a threat identified presents an opportunity to counteract it. New opportunities must be listed (see *Figure 8.2*).

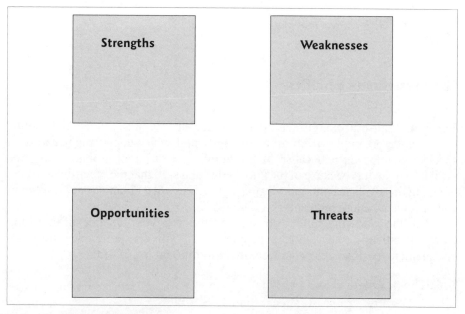

Figure 8.1: SWOT analysis

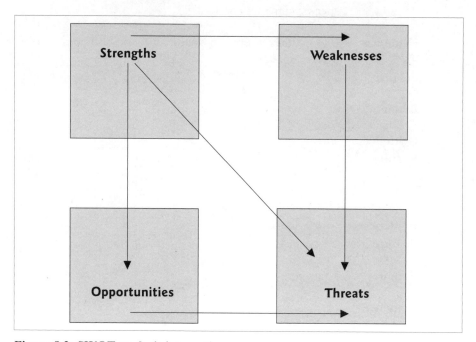

Figure 8.2: SWOT analysis interaction

SWOT analysis requires the active interaction of every item on each list with every other list to ensure all aspects of the situation are covered (as shown). Compare each item with every other list and analyse what has been learnt about the situation, the likely actions, reactions and plans.

Features versus benefits

This is also a useful exercise, as people do not buy features – they buy benefits. Consider the example of an aromatherapist and why people might choose a specific practice. Is it because of the number of different aromatherapy oils available? No, it is because of the knowledge and skill that the practitioner has in blending those oils in a unique way to suit the individual client's specific ailment and provide a beneficial result (see *Table 8.1*).

Use the following table to consider what makes your practice different and more specifically why should people chose you in preference to other complementary practices or, indeed, more traditional forms of therapy.

Table 8.1: Features and benefits		
1.	Feature	20 different aromatherapy oils
	Benefit	Skill and knowledge to blend oils in a unique way to treat specific ailment beneficially
	Evidence	Case studies, client satisfaction surveys, testimonials, eg. letters of thanks
2.	Feature	
	Benefit	
	Evidence	
3.	Feature	
	Benefit	
	Evidence	
4.	Feature	
	Benefit	
	Evidence	

Research

Your market

Consider your market in terms of:

a) The people

- who are you aiming at: men, women?
- do they have specific requirements, eg. pregnancy, skin disorders, cardiovascular problems, disabilities?
- what age would they typically be?

b) The area

- geography – how far will they travel?
- location – are you easily accessible?
- how far is it feasible to travel if you are running a mobile practice?

Your competition

Who are your competitors? There are not only practices offering the same services as you do but other types of complementary therapists and more traditional practices.

It is always useful to find out what your competitors are doing in the marketplace to help you develop your own positioning in the market and identify a niche. Your starting point is your local *Yellow Pages*: look at the advertisements and what they say. How do they attempt to generate business? Look at their logo: what would it conjure up to you if you were a potential client. Note the addresses and visit them. Consider how their premises compare with yours. Ask for their literature.

Your offer

Ideally, you should base your offer on what your clients need and want.

If you already have clients you should undertake a customer satisfaction survey. If not, you could ask friends what they would look for from your type of practice.

The sort of questions you should ask are:

- what do you find attractive about our premises?
- do our opening times suit you? If not, what changes would you like to be made?
- are there any products or services we do not offer that you would like us to consider?
- do you go anywhere else for similar products or services? If so, why?
- how satisfied are you with the level of service and knowledge of our practitioners?
- how do you perceive our prices?
- how would you like to be kept informed of our offers etc?

You may wish to offer an incentive, eg. a free pen (any item that is given away should be branded with your logo).

These are just a few ideas that can form the basis of a valuable questionnaire. Even when your practice is up and running, you should do a similar survey from time to time to make sure that you are still offering your clients what they require. It will also help you build a clear picture of your customer profile and provide information to help with future promotions.

Having gathered as much information as possible about your market, your competition and what your offer should be, you can now begin to plan how you can best communicate with your potential clients.

Marketing plan

Objectives

Objectives are basically the things that you want to achieve through promotion. You should consider your objectives in the short, medium and long term. In order to help you consider your objectives, here are some standard ones but you should add your own. Note that objectives usually start with the word 'to'.

1. To raise awareness of your practice.
2. To inform your target market of the nature and range of your products and services.
3. To generate the optimum number of clients to utilise the hours available.
4. To generate income to sustain a marketing programme.
5. To attract additional practitioners.

Strategy

A strategy is the science and art of employing all the resources you have available to fulfil the objectives you have set yourself. Basically, it is a plan of how you intend to achieve those objectives. For example, the following strategies may be considered in answer to the above corresponding objectives:

1. By advertising in the local press.
2. By producing an informative leaflet.
3. By offering a special incentive to clients to take appointments at less popular times.
4. By allocating a proportion of each 'sale' to a marketing fund.
5. By networking.

(These are not the only solutions; they are merely given as examples.)

Targets

Set yourself achievable targets and constantly review progress against these.

Communication

Simply ask yourself the following:

- how can I best communicate with my identified target market?
- where is the best place to promote my message?
- when would be the most appropriate time?
- who should I be communicating with?
- what should I tell them?

Message

Consider carefully how you wish to be perceived. What do you want your target audience to know, think and feel about your practice, and what action do you want them to take as a result of your promotional activity?

Corporate identity

Every organisation has its own distinctive personality: it is the way in which its employees, customers, suppliers and the world perceive it. Corporate personality is what an organisation is all about – its values, attributes and the way it conducts business. The corporate identity is the visual manifestation of these factors. The design marks, colours and typefaces are a system of symbols by which people recognise us and what we stand for.

When you see the red and yellow colour scheme and the big 'M' of McDonald's™, you know exactly what to expect – not *haute cuisine* and not a transport café, but a certain quality of product and service.

The strength of a corporate identity lies not necessarily in the design, but in the consistency of application and maintenance. This applies to stationery, fascia signage, door plaques, interiors, vehicles, appointment cards, literature and advertising.

In developing your corporate identity think first what you stand for, how you would like to be perceived (eg. efficient, modern, quality, clean, clinical, friendly), then brief a design company to develop a logo in line with your strategy. Also, brief them on the required applications, as the design has to work across all communication material, ie. black and white versions for faxing. There is always more than one workable solution, so ask for three alternatives based on your brief, chose the one that you feel best suits the image you wish to portray (it may need further development or fine-tuning), then stick to it in everything you do. Do not compromise on the standards you have set yourself.

If you are providing anyone else with your logo, eg. for use in an exhibition catalogue or programme, make sure that you provide strict guidelines for its use. The design company who produced the identity will be able to help you here.

Tools

These include:

- advertising
- media relations
- direct marketing
- exhibitions and events
- literature
- referrals
- networking
- web-site.

Advertising: There are many different forms of advertising but we will confine ourselves to those most appropriate to promoting your practice. Advertising is a very effective way of reaching a large proportion of your target audience cost effectively. Your local newspaper or radio station will provide coverage of your geographical catchment area.

Leaflet drops are an excellent way of targeting areas of high potential. Identify likely areas by postcode. You can use a specialist company, the Royal Mail or your local freesheet newspaper to do this.

It is important to note that one advertisement doesn't make a campaign. Response to advertising can vary dependent upon the message and how receptive your target market is. It can take as many as seven hits before the message sinks in or before someone acts.

Advertising works if you have something interesting to say and you say it often enough. A one-off ad will have little impact.

The design and production of an advertisement is key. Make sure that your message benefits the customer. An ad that just says how wonderful you are and how 'proud to be associated' with a particular project rarely justifies the cost. Advertising is an ideas business: your message needs to be conveyed with freshness, originality and wit. It is advisable at this stage to call in the experts. Do not attempt to do it yourself; get a local designer to do it. A briefing form in the 'Act' section of this chapter (see *p.78*) will help you brief an advertising agency to produce an ad with impact.

When booking media space, choose your own subject and timing. Do not be drawn by special features run to generate income for the media owner.

Yellow Pages is also a good place to advertise. It provides an all year round reference point. Existing practices say that it generates a substantial proportion of leads. But make sure that you are in the right section. A new section for 'complementary therapies' has been added to the directory in 1999.

With regard to the ad design, again I suggest you go to a professional. Do not use the *Yellow Pages* design studio as you will get a poorly constructed ad using clip art that will not differentiate you from your competitors. Be consistent with all of your promotional material as it serves to constantly reinforce your image and message.

Media relations – guidance notes: There will be various reasons why you may wish to seek publicity and it is always important to set out what you hope to achieve. Remember that those who are responsible for putting together newspapers, magazines or television programmes will have their own agenda and you will need to show why your entry is of interest.

Journalists receive many media releases about organisations. However, it is widely known that media releases connected with specific events are more likely to get used for their immediacy. Having said that, it is always difficult to get releases through the stages of being noticed, read and then followed through to publication or usage – such is the nature of the business. It is extremely important to make your media releases as appealing as possible to the editor or programme producer and to send them to as many relevant media contacts as possible. Here are a few guidelines in writing effective media releases.

The following checklist is intended to help you decide how and who to approach. If you follow a few simple rules it will give you a better chance of achieving the desired coverage:

1. Identify the relevant media. Names and addresses are important – make sure they are up-to-date.
2. Decide what you are writing: is it a feature or is it a news item? Put yourself in the mind of the reader and it will make it easier to tell an interesting story and target the most appropriate publication.
3. When writing a media release it must be in plain English. Avoid abbreviations, technical terms and jargon, and don't forget to put your main point first. Editors are busy people and will glance quickly at a media release to see if anything interesting catches their eye. If you miss the initial impact your release goes into the bin.
4. Notes to editors provide useful background information.
5. Accuracy is absolutely essential. When using names give both first and surnames and make sure that they are spelt correctly.
6. Always include a contact name, telephone number and fax number so that the editors know where to go for clarification and more information. Be sure to include the organisation's name and address for reader enquiries. Make sure that those concerned are contactable. One name is sufficient. Clearly note daytime and evening telephone numbers.
7. Write separate media releases on individual subjects. A single release listing all your organisation's activities will lose impact when being read by an editor.
8. The title of a media release should convey precisely what makes the release worth using.
9. Always use double line spacing – this will help those who edit the release, and make it quicker and easier to read.
10. The first paragraph should encapsulate the whole story and grab the reader's attention at the same time. Subsequent paragraphs should give further depth and detail to the initial paragraph.
11. Quote any relevant facts and figures, which will add depth to your story.

12. Be bold – don't hype your story but there are no prizes for modesty.
13. Photographs must be of sufficient quality for good reproduction. Do not expect to get them back. If your photographs are 'home' shots make sure that composition has been considered. Include photographs where possible. Label them on the back; never staple them to the release. Provide a caption.
14. If you have a big story follow it up to establish whether the publication intend to use it. Ask if they need any more information.
15. Appearing in front on a television camera can be a daunting experience and the image presented will reflect not just on the person concerned but on the whole organisation. You need to ensure that you have a well-briefed and articulate spokesperson. Training with a home video can work wonders.
16. Old news is no news – you must be up-to-date. This is not to say that you cannot write a feature after an event but you will need to prove that it is relevant for publication in the paper or magazines you have chosen to target.
17. If you have an exceptional story to tell, or wish to ensure that you get the maximum publicity, you should consult a PR expert.
18. It is important that you put yourself into the mind of your audience and that you provide clear and accessible information in your area and present your case accordingly.

Press cuttings can be a useful source when you are asked to demonstrate your track record, so it is important to monitor press coverage and keep a clippings file. There are commercial organisations that will do this for you, but they tend to be inexpensive.

You can use your media releases and press cuttings as mailers to your client database (see 'Direct marketing' below). Place a copy of your clippings file in your reception area for clients to read while they are waiting; it will reassure them that they have made the right choice in coming to your practice.

Direct marketing: The first step is to create a customer/potential customer database. You should also include 'non-customer influencials' such as GPs, your bank manager, accountant and solicitor, as it is important to keep all interested parties informed of what you are offering and how the business is doing. It may also result in referrals.

Ideally, you should build your database on a computer, as this makes it more manageable. Database software can be bought relatively inexpensively but make sure it has a search facility, keyword facility, reports facility, notepad, mail merge and word processing and preferably a time-management system so that you can record what you have sent to whom and when further activity is required.

You should record the following information on the database:

- client's name (check spellings of difficult names)
- address (check spellings of difficult words)
- telephone number
- facsimile if available
- e-mail if available
- date of birth

- source (where the client has come from, eg. were they recommended by another client?) and the date they first became a client or showed an interest
- do they use any other practice for similar therapies and if so, which?
- how regularly they attend
- what other therapies/products have they bought?
- links with other customers: have they recommended anyone else?
- status, ie. whether they are a current, past or potential client.

Once you have built your initial database it becomes a useful tool to send out targeted information, ie:

- special offers (eg. recommend a friend and receive a discounted treatment yourself)
- questionnaires
- seasonal greetings
- birthday greetings with offer
- gifts
- free samples
- copies of your media releases and articles published
- information cards (detailing opening hours etc)
- information on advancements or treatments
- relevant news articles
- invitations to events
- a newsletter – your professional body may produce regular newsletters that you can purchase in bulk, overprint with your details and mail out to your database
- postcards for keeping in touch.

One of the key advantages of building a database is to introduce a loyalty scheme to generate more business from existing clients. It is always easier and cheaper to generate more business from people who are already 'sold' on your practice than to constantly be looking to expand your customer base.

Don't blanket mail your database. Direct marketing is about building one-to-one relationships with your customers and tailoring your offer to their individual needs. Remember that your most valuable customer is the one you already have and it is cheaper to retain that customer than to court a new one.

It is important to note that a database is constantly evolving as you add, delete and amend entries. The best way of keeping it up-to-date is through constant use; otherwise, as much as 75% of your list could be out-of-date within 12 months.

Make sure you register with the Office of the Data Protection Registrar (see *Appendix I*, 'Useful addresses').

Exhibitions and events: Exhibiting yourself and your practice could range from a national trade show to a local village fête, but the same rules apply.

Exhibitions can take a big slice of your budget. You may be competing head to head with your competitors for attention. Make sure that you have something to say and that your stand is eye-catching and reflects the image you wish to communicate. Think carefully about the position of your stand before booking: make sure you are in a main thoroughfare and not tucked away in some corner where no one will see you. Put as much into the pre-show preparation and the post-show follow-up as you do into the show itself.

The following provides a checklist of activities to consider when exhibiting:

- stand positioning
- allocate budget
- decide on product display
- order and prepare exhibits
- stand design
- order services
- select and train staff
- order tickets and passes
- write to your database inviting them to visit your stand
- prepare media release
- decide on other promotional activity surrounding the exhibition
- photograph stand for media release
- prepare literature and hand-outs
- make sure your entry in the catalogue is correct.

You may wish to hold an event yourself, for example, to celebrate your opening, or a seasonal celebration, eg. Christmas. The following checklist provides areas for consideration:

- venue – preferably at your premises
- invitations – should be in your corporate style
- allocate budget
- staffing
- catering
- how you intend to sell your products and services
- special incentives to commit at the event
- send invitations to people on your database – plus bring a friend
- capturing information on new prospect for inclusion on your database
- name badges
- prepare pre-event media release
- plan photograph of the event for post-event release
- prepare literature and hand-outs
- prepare a short welcome speech
- send letter and information about the event to those unable to attend.

Literature: Most practices have some form of leaflet detailing their services. It basically serves as an information leaflet for clients.

When planning the format consider how the leaflet is to be used. Is it something that needs to be easily slipped into a pocket or handbag? What information will your clients need to know from you? (Remember your features and benefits?)

Keep it simple and easy to read. Do not use jargon or difficult medical terminology. Make it user-friendly. The design should incorporate your corporate values and identity.

Print can be relatively inexpensive but consider the use of colour as a four-colour print job will be more expensive than two. Shop around – a local franchise operation such as ProntaPrint will provide you with a good price guide.

Referrals: It is likely that once you establish a reputation a high proportion of your business will come through recommendations. Rather than leaving this to fate you should capitalise on this as a marketing opportunity. Think of ways you can influence these people to recommend you over other practices.

Referrals may come from a number of different areas. Firstly, it is quite a simple process to influence existing clients to refer a friend through offers, the service you provide and the advice you give.

If you believe that GPs, for example, are your main source of referral you need to consider ways of influencing them. This could be done by:

- providing reference literature
- something three dimensional with your logo and telephone number for their desk as a constant reminder
- meetings to inform them of your services and how they can benefit their patients
- seminars at surgeries to educate interested patients
- posters on notice boards in waiting rooms.

Tools	1.		2.	
Target	Advantages	Disadvantages	Advantages	Disadvantages
1.				
2.				
3.				
4.				
5.				

Figure 8.3: Promotional activity and analysis

Networking: Networking means simply contacting people you already know and meeting new people who may have an interest in your practice. The secret is to keep in contact with these people; you never know when they may have a need to use your services. All contact names and details should be added to your database for mailing purposes.

Website: Marketing on the Internet is constantly evolving and it is therefore difficult to advise about it in the static format of a book and remain current, but here are some pointers. The best and most up-to-date advice can be accessed via the net itself. There may be directories provided by your own professional organisations where you can get a listing. If you have a website or e-mail address make sure it is visible on all printed material including stationery, leaflets and advertising. At this stage in its development you may be just as well seeking advice from a useful friend, not so much on the screen designs but how the information should be structured and accessed.

Budget

All of these ideas will not cost a fortune if you plan in advance, adapt them in line with your ongoing research and don't get drawn into other activities unless it will make a positive contribution to your business.

Your initial plan should include likely costs and you should consider if they are affordable at that stage and then prioritise accordingly. Remember to obtain firm quotes from consultants and suppliers and always negotiate with the media.

As a general rule of thumb you should allocate between one and two per cent of your sales/forecast sales to marketing your business.

Act

Action plan

Figure 8.4 (opposite) has been provided to help you prepare your own plan of action.

Writing a brief

Briefing a specialist is all-important. Providing an accurate brief means that the end result should be in line with your thinking. A bad brief could prove a costly exercise. Use *Figure 8.5 (p.78)* to help you provide an outside specialist with the information he or she requires.

| Action plan | | | | | | Issued by: |
| | | | | | | Date: |
	Activity	Action required	Measure of success	By whom	By when	Completed
1						
2						
3						
4						
5						
6						
7						
8						
9						
10						
11						
12						
13						
14						
15						
16						

Figure 8.4: Action plan

Brief to outside specialist	
Practice:	Contact name:
	Telephone:
Activity title:	Date:
What job is this trying to do?	
The target audience	
What should they know, think and feel when they see it?	
Single proposition	
What evidence do we have?	
Media type	
Budget	
Previous activity – when, where, how often	
Mandatory inclusions – logos, phone numbers, names etc.	
Desired image – friendly, sophisticated, contemporary etc.	
Required by date:	
Supplementary information attached: yes/no	

Figure 8.5: Brief to outside specialist

Schedule of activity

The following schedule of activity (*Figure 8.6, opposite*) should help you keep track of your budget and where your money is being spent.

Office		Campaign		Period											
Activity	Medium	Cost	J	F	M	A	M	J	J	A	S	O	N	D
Total															

Figure 8.6: Schedule of activity

When to call in the experts

The advent of computer technology, specifically desk-top publishing and clip-art, has brought some of the tools of publicity and promotion to small businesses. However, this is like providing a palette of paints to an unskilled artist and asking him or her to paint a masterpiece. You may have the tools but not necessarily the skills. Stick to what you are good at and use your knowledge of your business and your marketplace to brief professionals to prepare designs and advertising for you. Brief them properly and provide a budget to work to.

Selecting the right experts to suit your purposes can be difficult. The best way is by referral. Ask people whose opinion you respect, eg. your bank manager, to recommend a local design agency for your corporate identity, an advertising agency to produce your advertising and a PR agency to write media releases for you. Beware of companies who say that they can do everything unless they are a full-service agency with expertise in all aspects of marketing. When selecting the best partner to work with, ask to see their credentials – what have they done for other organisations of a similar size?

Measurement and monitoring

Spend a few hours each month assessing your marketing activity and monitoring the changes. Measure these changes against your objectives. Simple measurements can be made against specific activities such as the increase in telephone enquiries, special offer coupon redemptions and asking new customers where they have heard about you. By doing this your marketing pound will work harder. You will learn what works best and why and it will help you convert more enquiries into business. It will also help you to plan your future marketing activity more effectively.

Exercises

1. Work through the SWOT analysis for yourself.
2. Make your own draft action plan.
3. Plan the information and format your promotional leaflet and what you would include.

Relevant draft unit from National Occupational Standards (NOS)

C4 plan the marketing strategy for the business

Elements of competence:

C4.1 Assess the results of market research relevant to the proposed business venture.

C4.2 Identify options for effective marketing of business.

C4.3 Produce a marketing plan.

The above is concerned with detailed and specific marketing for the business and requires the therapist to:

- evaluate available market research
- identify and evaluate options for marketing the business
- produce a detailed marketing plan for the business.

This unit is aimed at the person with responsibility for the market strategy of the business.

References

National Occupational Standards (1997) *Consortium Pack, Section B, Setting up Practice Units*. Written for the Care Sector Consortium. Distributed by Prime Research and Development Ltd, Harrogate

This chapter (excluding information on NOS) was contributed by Nicola Evans of Evans Whalley Ltd, Marketing Consultants (see Useful addresses).

9

Health and safety

This is a general introduction to the issue of health and safety as different therapies will have wildly differing risks in this area – for example, the disposal of needles for acupuncture or the use of possibly hazardous essential oils in aromatherapy.

For the purposes of this chapter 'employer' refers to self-employed practitioners and homeworkers.

The Health and Safety at Work Act of 1974 (HSWA) places duties on employers, self-employed people and employees. Under HSWA, employers have a duty to protect the health, safety and welfare of the employees, including homeworkers. Most of the regulations made under the HSWA apply to home-workers as well as to employees working at an employer's workplace. These include, for example, the Management of Health and Safety at Work Regulations 1992, the Display Screen Equipment Regulations 1992, the Manual Handling Operations Regulations 1992, the Provision and Use of Work Equipment Regulations 1992 and the Control of Substances Hazardous to Health Regulations 1994 (COSHH).

Under the Management of Health and Safety at Work Regulations 1992, employers are required to do a risk assessment that includes the work activities carried out by homeworkers. Completing a risk assessment involves identifying the hazards involved in work activities and deciding whether enough steps have been taken to prevent harm to them or anyone else who may be affected by their work. A risk is the chance, great or small, that someone will be harmed by a hazard. A hazard is anything that may cause harm.

How to do a risk assessment

(website source: www.open.gov.uk/hse/pubns)

There are five steps that employers, including those who are self-employed or working from home, need to take to make sure that a proper risk assessment is done:

1. Identify any hazards

It is the employer's duty to look at what may cause harm to any employees or other people as a result of the work being done in the home. Small hazards should not be ignored as they may result in harm; for example, potentially harmful substances must be kept out of children's reach.

2. Decide who might be harmed and how

Employers must look at who might be affected by the work carried out at the practice and how they may be affected. This may affect a homeworker and members of the household, including children or visitors.

3. Assess the risks and take appropriate action

If employers come across a hazard that may be a risk, they need to decide what steps have to be taken to eliminate or reduce those risks as far as possible. What needs to be done depends on whether the hazard is low risk or high risk. Employers can determine this by looking at what type of harm or injury may arise and how often it may happen. For example, there is a greater risk of accident from loose trailing wires if there are children in the home.

Employers may be able to remove the hazard altogether or take steps to lower the risk to an acceptable level. For example, loose wires from work equipment could be tucked away under a desk or table, or secured neatly round the furniture out of the way.

If there is no risk present, no action needs to be taken by the employer. To check if the risks are acceptable, employers can get more information about legal standards from *Essentials of Health and Safety at Work HSE* (1994).

4. Recording the findings

Employers who have five or more employees, including homeworkers, are required by law to record the significant findings from a risk assessment. They need to note what steps have been taken and tell anyone affected by the work being done about the findings.

5. Check the risks at regular intervals and take steps if needed

It is important for employers to check the risk assessment from time to time, especially if there is a change in working procedures. The assessment needs to take into account any new hazards that may cause harm to the health or safety of any people affected by the change in working conditions.

General health and safety considerations for the treatment room

Temperature

The working temperature should be comfortable – probably around 16–20°C, optimum 18°C. Heating apparatus should be checked regularly, but most importantly not be dangerous or give off offensive fumes. Remember, if your client has to undress they will feel cooler than you do.

Air

There should be enough ventilation to remove smells and to keep air circulating. Stale air will make the therapist and client feel tired and listless. Sweat will not readily evaporate from the skin surface and your client may feel uncomfortable.

Lighting

This should be bright enough for safety but not so bright as to cause glare. Natural daylight is always best, and would even be considered essential for assessing skin pallor and condition. Remember, poor light can cause eyestrain and headaches. The client and therapist should not be dazzled by bright lights. Any flickering bulbs should be replaced immediately.

Sanitary and washing facilities

Wherever you choose to work you need these facilities adjacent to your treatment room. It is preferable to have hand-washing facilities within the treatment room. Remember, stagnant water smells unpleasant and increases bacterial growth and disease. If you have a blocked sink or drains you should not work until this has been cleared. Report any strange-coloured or smelling water to your local water authority.

Fire extinguishers and fire alarms

The Fire Precautions Act 1971,1976 states that a fire certificate is necessary if more than 10 people are in the building anywhere except on the ground floor, or if more than 20 people are employed. This is obtainable from the local fire authority. Smaller clinics or home treatment rooms should ensure that there is:

- fire-fighting equipment for both electrical and chemical fires, which is checked regularly
- a signed, easily accessible, speedy exit
- working, well-placed fire alarms.

Illness

If you have an infectious illness or skin condition that could spread to your clients or work colleagues **do not work**. It is irresponsible and unacceptable to work with even something as seemingly mild as a cold, especially as most therapists work in close contact with clients, often in a confined space.

Some common hazards in the workplace

Handling loads

Handling loads can cause serious injury, particularly to the back. The checklist below highlights some activities that may increase the risk:

- handling loads that are heavy, bulky, difficult to grasp, or unstable
- awkward lifting, reaching or handling
- pushing or pulling
- repetitive handling that does not allow enough rest time between loads
- twisting and stooping.

Employers should avoid the need for hazardous manual handling. However, if this cannot be avoided, employers are responsible for assessing and reducing the risks, for example by providing training and/or lifting aids to prevent injury. This could involve using a trolley to allow the load to be moved easily. Guidelines for handling and moving goods are covered by Manual Handling Operations Regulations 1992. Common sense measures such as lifting or carrying goods in small amounts, wrapping the load or using gloves if it has sharp edges, or using a table or bench as a half-way resting point are good techniques to adopt to help reduce risks.

Using work equipment at home

The Provision and Use of Work Equipment Regulations 1992 cover the use of work equipment in the home. The safe use of electricity at work is covered by the Electricity at Work Regulations 1989 but most of the faults in electrical equipment that can cause harm can be prevented just by checking for any damage to that equipment on a regular basis. Listed below are simple steps that can be taken to prevent harm or injury in this area:

- ensure electrical equipment is turned off before it is checked
- check that plugs are not damaged
- check that the electrical systems are adequate for electrical equipment (especially if working from home)
- check plugs are correctly wired and maintained
- check that the outer covering of the cable or wire is gripped where it enters the plug or the equipment
- check that the outer cover of the equipment is not damaged – for example, look for loose parts or screws
- check leads, wires or cables for damage to the outer covering
- check for burn marks or staining that suggests overheating
- check that there are no trailing wires; if there are, tuck them out of the way to prevent accidents.

Working with VDUs

Although it is unlikely that the therapist will spend many hours every day in front of the monitor, the secretary or receptionist employed by the self-employed therapist may do so and the therapist is ultimately responsible. The use of VDUs is covered by the Health and Safety (Display Screen Equipment) Regulations 1992. Employers have a duty to make sure that the display screen equipment used, including the use by homeworkers, is safe and does not affect the user's health. When working with VDUs it is important to adjust the work station to a comfortable position and take breaks from work. This will help prevent undue tiredness. Similarly, stretching and changing position regularly can help reduce tiredness and prevent pains in the hands, wrists, arms, neck, shoulders or back. VDUs need to be placed in a position where lighting will not cause reflections or glare on the screen. It may be the case that employees need different spectacles for viewing the screen comfortably and VDU users can request an eye examination paid for by their employer.

Here is a checklist of points to be aware of when using VDUs:

- is the screen clear and readable, and without flicker? Is the screen free from glare and reflections?
- are the 'brightness' and 'contrast' controls properly adjusted to prevent eyestrain?
- is there suitable lighting so that the fine detail on the screen can be seen and read?
- is the keyboard placed in the right position to allow the work to be undertaken comfortably?
- is the screen and computer clean: are they free from dust and dirt?
- can the chair be adjusted to the right height so that work can be done comfortably?
- is the VDU placed at the right angle on the desk to allow work to be done comfortably, for example, without having to make any awkward movements?
- is there enough space under the desk to allow free movement?
- is there enough space in general so that the homeworker can move freely between the work on the desk and the VDU?

New and expectant mothers

New legislation required to implement the European Directive on Pregnant Workers was introduced into the Management of Health and Safety at Work Regulations 1992 by the Management of Health and Safety at Work (Amendment) Regulations 1994 with effect from 1 December 1994. When assessing risks, the new legislation requires the employer to pay attention to workers who are new and expectant mothers. Risks include those to the unborn child or to the child of a woman who is still breast feeding – not just risks to the mother herself. A new or expectant mother means a worker who is pregnant, who has given birth within the previous six months, or who is breast feeding. 'Given birth' is defined in the new Regulations as 'delivered a living child or, after 24 weeks of pregnancy, a stillborn child'.

Therapists who use essential oils should protect any employee or client falling into the category of new and expectant mothers from exposure to essential oils with any contraindications.

New and Expectant Mothers at Work: A guide for employees sets out the known risks to new and expectant mothers and gives advice on what the employer is required to do to comply with health and safety laws.

First Aid

Under the Health and Safety (First Aid) Regulations 1981, employers need to ensure that they have adequate first aid provisions, including supplying homeworkers. A statutory first aid box should be kept in or next to the treatment room and contents should be regularly updated.

The exact provisions depend on the nature of the work activity and the risks involved. Further information is available in *First Aid at Work*. Many professional organisations in complementary therapies insist that practitioners have a current first aid certificate, a minimum six-hour 'appointed person training'. As well as being a professional responsibility, this is a personal duty to your clients.

Reporting of injuries, diseases and dangerous occurrences

The revised Reporting of Injuries, Diseases and Dangerous Occurrences Regulations 1995 (RIDDOR 95) came into force on 1 April 1996 (previously RIDDOR 1985). These Regulations place a duty on the employer to report and keep a record of certain work-related accidents, injuries, diseases and dangerous occurrences. Employers have a duty to find out about accidents, injuries, diseases or dangerous occurrences arising from work-related activities. This may involve ensuring that homeworkers report any incidents to their employer. *RIDDOR: Everyone's guide to RIDDOR 95* gives advice on what employers need to do to comply. You may be self-employed and working alone; however, if you use your home or lease or purchase premises, your local council environmental services have a right to visit and to report on any premises used for a business with a view to making recommendations to improve any potential hazards under this act.

Health and safety executive (HSE) inspectors

HSE inspectors enforce the HSWA and the Regulations made under the HSWA. Inspectors visit employers (and also have the right to visit homeworkers) to ensure that risks from work and working at home are properly managed. They also investigate and help settle complaints about working conditions that could affect the health, safety or welfare of employees, including anyone who works from home.

Using substances and materials

Complementary therapists should be aware of The Control Of Substances Hazardous to Health COSHH 1994 Regulations. Many therapists use lotions, oils or gels with plant derivatives, which may have known hazards. COSHH states that effects of hazardous substances include:

- skin irritation, dermatitis or even skin cancer from frequent contact
- asthma
- toxic fumes
- poisoning by ingestion
- infection from bacteria and other micro-organisms.

COSHH requires that a risk assessment is carried out to cover all possible hazardous substances. The therapist should consider whether a substance is a hazard, ie. whether it has the potential to cause harm as in the case of essential oils if incorrectly used, or a risk, ie. whether it has a likelihood of causing harm.

An easy way of identifying hazardous substances is by looking for hazard warnings on the label. The Chemicals (Hazardous Information and Packaging for Supply) Regulations 1994 (CHIP2) require hazardous substances to be labelled with orange and black hazard symbols. Any substance that places people's health or safety at risk must be handled according to the instructions provided by the employer, the supplier of work or the manufacturer or supplier of the substance. Here is a checklist of things to be aware of when using substances, materials or chemicals in your practice:

- are they flammable, toxic or corrosive?
- do they give off fumes?
- are they stored safely? For example, could any children reach them easily?
- does anyone suffer from dizzy spells, feel sick or have headaches when in the vicinity of these substances?
- does anyone suffer from skin rashes or irritation?
- does anyone suffer from asthma?

If the risk assessment shows that a person's health is at risk from exposure to any hazardous substance, the employer must take appropriate action.

In 1998 the area of COSHH and aromatherapy was looked at in some depth by Fowler and Wall, who stated that 'essential oils contain substances which may be detrimental to health; as such, they are subject to COSHH and CHIPS regulations'. Their paper outlines an approach for applying these to the area of aromatherapy (Fowler and Wall, 1998).

Examples of assessment and risk forms should ask such questions as:

- name of oil and supplier?
- hazardous classification?
- how much is used?
- how frequently?
- how is it applied?

- who is exposed and are any vulnerable persons exposed, eg. pregnant women?
- length of exposure time, eg. up to 30 minutes/1–2 hours?
- frequency of time exposed, eg. daily/ weekly?

Therapists who use essential oils should request a *CHIP 96 data sheet* which will enable them to complete relevant risk assessments.

Considering many therapists, including Reiki healers, crystal therapists, osteopaths and others, in addition to aromatherapists now use essential oils, the impact of these guidelines for safety will have a greater effect, particularly where therapies are used in a hospital setting.

See also the sample 'Hospital protocol' example in *Chapter 5 (pp.43–44)* , and the sample COSHH assessment form for carrier and essential oils *(pp. 90–91)*. (The COSHH form has been developed from an example given by Fowler and Wall, 1998.)

Further information on health and safety

If you have a problem with health and safety, further advice is available from your local HSE officer (see under Health and Safety Executive in your local telephone directory). Trade Unions and regional home working projects can also offer advice if applicable to your particular working circumstances.

Exercises

1. Practise carrying out a risk assessment in your home, carefully recording your findings.
2. If you use any substances which may require a COSHH assessment (eg. essential oils), copy the sample form and complete it using relevant information from a CHIP data sheet and information from text books.
3. Contact the council Environmental Health Department for advice.

COSHH hazard assessment for carrier and essential oils

Oil(s) details			Oil name(s) (trade/generic)		
Manufacturer (who made it)			Supplier (Who sold it)		
Hazard classification (see safety data sheet) Risk/safety phrases					
How much is used? (insert mls)	Per day		Per week	Per month	Other
How frequently used (circle)	Daily		Weekly	Monthly	Other
How is it contacted? (circle)		Eyes	Skin	Ingestion	Inhalation	Other
Who is exposed? (circle)	Therapist / patient-client / staff / student / others				
Is there potential for pregnant women to be exposed?				Yes ☐	No ☐
Safe dilution recommended?			Actual dilution used?		

Length of exposure? (insert daily, weekly, monthly, annual, other)		
Time	**Therapist**	**Others (list)**
Up to 30 mins		
30 mins – I hour		
I – 4 hours		
4 – 8 hours		
Maximum exposure limit (M.E.L.) (daily):		

Potential effects of exposure

eye burn irritation	☐	breathlessness	☐	nausea	☐	drowsiness	☐
photosensitiser	☐	skin-burn/ irritation	☐	carcinogen	☐	other	☐

Any other likely hazards?

Source of safety information?

COSHH hazard assessment for carrier and essential oils (contin.)

Control measures (tick)	In place (can be seen)	Needed (to be done)	Not needed	Comments
Enclosed treatment area				
Restricted access				
General ventilation*				
Local exhaust ventilation*				
Oils mixed as proceeding				
Spillage kit and procedure				
Data sheets for all oils				
Data sheets with spills kit				
Flammable store cabinet				
Store locked and signposted				
Containers labelled				
Waste separated				
Flammables waste bin				
Fire extinguisher				
No smoking enforced				
First Aid, eyewash/water				
PPE (gloves, apron, mask)				
Hand-washing facilities				
Laundering				
Client given safety info.				

*Dates of electrical and operational maintenance must be recorded for ventilation systems.

Overall risk judgement

Due to the above precautions and arrangements, the risk of harm from the oil(s) in this assessment is:

High (extensive □   Medium □   Low (little □
control measures needed)   (recognised hazard)   or no hazard)

Declaration

This assessment was carried out on (date):   By (print name):

Qualifications: Signature:

References

Fowler P, Wall N (1998) Complementary Therapies in Medicine. *Aromatherapy Control of Substances Hazardous to Health and Assessment of the Chemical Risk.* **6**: 85–93

Birmingham City Council's Economic Development Unit Health & Safety Connections: *Health & Safety Help-line leaflet. Birmingham B1 3BR*

COSSH & CHIPS. HMSO Stationers. Also at website: www.open.gov.uk /hse/pubns/coshh2.htm

Useful publications (health and safety)

The Complete Idiot's Guide to CHIP 2 IND(G)181L

COSHH: A brief guide for employers IND(G)136L

Display Screen Equipment Work. Health and Safety Display Screen Equipment Regulations 1992. Guidance on Regulations: ISBN 0 717604101

Electricity at Work: Safe working practices HS(G)85: ISBN 0 71760442X

Essentials of Health and Safety at Work (1994) HSE Books: ISBN 0 71760716X

First-aid Needs in Your Workplace: Your questions answered IND(G)L (revised) (free)

First Aid at Work Health and Safety (First-Aid) Regulations 1981. Approved Code of Practice and Guidance: ISBN 0717604268

5 Steps to Risk Assessment IND(G)163L (free)

General COSHH ACOP (Control of substances hazardous to health), Carcinogens ACOP (Control of carcinogenic substances) and Biological agents ACOP (Control of biological agents). Control of Substances Hazardous to Health Regulations 1994. Approved Code of Practice 1995: ISBN 0 717608190

Getting to Grips with Manual Handling IND(G)143L (free)

A Guide to the Reporting of Injuries, Diseases and Dangerous Occurrences Regulations 1995 (RIDDOR): ISBN 0717610128

Manual Handling. Manual Handling Operations Regulations 1992. Guidance on Regulations: ISBN 0 71760411X

Management of Health and Safety at Work. Management of Health and Safety at Work Regulations 1992. Approved Code of Practice 1992: ISBN 0 717614128

Memorandum of Guidance on the Electricity at Work Regulations 1989: ISBN 0118839632

New and Expectant Mothers at Work: A guide for employers HS(G)122: ISBN 0717608263

Personal Protective Equipment at Work. Personal Protective Equipment at Work Regulations 1992. Guidance on Regulations: ISBN 0 717604152

RIDDOR: Everyone's guide to RIDDOR 95 HSE31 (free)

Safety Representatives and Safety Committees: ISBN 0717604195

Work equipment. Provision and Use of Work Equipment Regulations 1992. Guidance on Regulations: ISBN 0 7176 04144

Working with VDUs IND(G)36L (free)

VDUs: An Easy Guide to the Regulations HS(G)90: ISBN 0 717607356

HSE priced and free publications are available by mail order from HSE Books (see *Appendix I,* 'Useful addresses'). Priced publications are also available from good bookstores. Most of the information in this section has been sourced from the HSE's web page and other enquiries can be addressed to the HSE's information centre (see *Appendix I,* 'Useful addresses').

Your local council may also be a useful source of guidance and information on the subject of health and safety. Birmingham City Council, for example, offer independent advice on workplace health and safety issues for an annual fee currently equivalent to £1.00 per week. In return they provide a year-round 24-hour helpline to help reduce risk in the workplace and establish safer working practices. Environmental health officers frequently visit premises to carry out spot-checks in regard to the Health and Safety at Work Act 1974 so it would be wise to contact the Council's Environmental Health Department relevant to your practice to see what advice they can offer.

10

Summary and thoughts for the future

As we move into the twenty-first century there are new challenges for complementary and alternative medicines (CAM) and its practitioners. Recent initiatives indicate that CAM will become progressively more integrated into orthodox medicine. Therapists may work alongside orthodox health practitioners or many more orthodox health carers will acquire and practise CAM skills. Towards the end of the twentieth century we saw the development of the 'Foundation for Integrated Healthcare', often known as 'FIM' (Foundation for Integrated Medicine). FIM published the document *A Way Forward for the Next 5 Years* in 1997. At the end of 1999, CAM organisations had a 'call for evidence' from the House of Lords Science and Technology sub-committee (Makower, 1999). Following their call, the British Medical Association (BMA) gave a press release and an initiative calling for ' a single regulating body to be established for each therapy'. They also stated that, 'CAM should be regulated to change the current unacceptable situation in which for most therapies virtually anyone is free to practice irrespective of his or her training' (BMA, 1999).

Reviewing these documents and observing the growth of CAM at this time, it would appear that we are here to stay and that the integration process is underway. We also have the opportunity to be accepted by all facets of health providers.

The FIM (1997) discussion document *A Way Forward for the Next 5 Years* evolved, along with the actual foundation itself, following suggestions from the Prince of Wales. The Royal Family is well known for its support of CAM and this factor has influenced a large sector of the population, both directly and through the media.

The proposals within the document, which reports the conclusions of four working groups under the guidance of a steering committee, are to consider the positions of CAM and orthodox medicine in the UK. Their recommendations include:

- establishing research centres for CAM
- prioritising research and development
- assessing the needs of provision
- ensuring greater understanding and education of CAM to medical and other healthcare students and vice versa
- encouraging common core elements of education, including subjects such as pathology
- the provision of better information for patients, professionals and policy makers
- encouraging regulation within CAM
- surveying existing practice to produce best practice guidelines.

(FIM 1997, p.3)

As we enter the new millennium, this five-year plan is unfolding and progressing in support of the above. A growing number of Universities are now offering CAM degree courses (see *Appendix V*).

Research projects and trials are underway at many major hospitals and universities. According to a recent newsletter from FIM (1999) a recent survey revealed that one in five respondents had used CAM in the last year as follows:

Herbal medicine	34%
Aromatherapy	21%
Homeopathy	17%
Acupuncture and acupressure	15%
Reflexology	6%
Massage	6%
Osteopathy	4%

Eighty per cent of all respondents believed that CAM would continue to increase in popularity.

The key message from the BMA press release on 1 November 1999 is possibly twofold, the first emphasising that as an orthodox medical organisation they are definitely very aware of complementary therapists and CAM. This awareness has now prompted their interest and concern. Secondly, their points are well founded as, quite apart from protecting the public's interests, a GP is ultimately responsible for managing a patient's care. If any advice or information on a therapy has been given to a patient by a GP, the GP needs to review the effect of the CAM treatment. GPs also need to assure themselves of research into efficacy and safety to an acceptable level, as they should with orthodox treatments. However, perhaps it should be considered that, according to FIM, 75% of orthodox medical prescriptions within the NHS are not researched (FIM conference, 1998).

The document also insists that NHS provision of CAM should be confined to those areas of CAM where a formal regulatory system exists. Further points echo the FIM initiatives calling for:

- more support and funding of research and organisations such as the Research Council for Complementary Medicine (RCCM)
- evidence of efficacy
- regulation of each therapy
- competent standards of training.

There is still some controversy between various organisations about whether one single umbrella body over all forms of non-conventional medicine should be established or a single regulatory body of each therapy.

As osteopathy and chiropractic are now regulated by statute, and other professional organisations are halfway to establishing their discretionary regulatory body, it would seem probable that the single regulatory body for each therapy is preferable (as called for by the BMA).

Such initiatives for greater regulation and proof of efficacy were bound to arise with the increase in popularity of CAM. If they respond in a professional and organised way, CAM practitioners can establish themselves within the framework of healthcare provision throughout the twenty-first century and beyond.

Over recent years there has already been an enormous shift in attitude towards CAM and provision is now made in hospitals such as University Hospital, Birmingham for oncology patients to receive CAM treatments.

This new era sees the public being less accepting than they used to be. People no longer accept everything that their GP tells them, but are better informed and more likely to ask questions. We are bombarded with information and generally encouraged to use a telephone help-line or pharmacy rather than visit a GP.

Due to changes in education and the media, we all have a far greater understanding of the human body, pathology and healthcare, and we question the wisdom of antibiotics and invasive treatments. In general, with the increase of information available to the population, there has been an increase in criticism and dissatisfaction with healthcare provision, which may have been inevitable.

The increase in the popularity of CAM coincides with the above. Many people want more control over life strategies, empowerment and personal choices. It is also apparent that whatever the advances in orthodox medicine, we as a global population continue to experience illness, new diseases and disorders, and are threatened by resistant micro-organisms. This leaves an open door for continuing alternatives. The cost of drugs may also make natural alternatives more favourable.

CAM is also often seen as prophylactic and preventative, which allows for greater tolerance among certain health practitioners who may not see CAM as offering effective treatments, but can live with the perception of its being 'stress-relieving' or offering 'enhanced well being'. So, the future of CAM integrated into orthodox medicine and the NHS is a strong possibility.

Will there be independent therapists and practices in the future? This is a question many 'non-nurse' therapists might be considering. It would seem that there will always be a place for independent health practitioners. Take physiotherapists, chiropractors, etc. within the NHS and in private practices everywhere. Independent CAM practices offer excellent services and facilities, and CAM practitioners and similar therapists may work partly in each sector. Private insurance policies can now cover CAM provision. The therapist who works in a poky back bedroom for 'a little bit of pocket money' with no desire to upgrade his or her skills and no intention of practising in a professional or informed way is definitely on the way out!

Finally, it is in our own hands as therapists to ensure our future, to encourage and support the organisations that are striving to develop a single regulatory body for each therapy – such as the Aromatherapy Organisation's Council (AOC) for aromatherapy – and to encourage the formation of a single national register of members only open to properly trained therapists. To take part in research projects and support others who are trying to provide evidence of efficacy. To ensure our own level and duration of training will stand up to scrutiny. To abide by and promote an enforceable code of conduct and ethics supported by a disciplinary procedure.

Throughout this book it has been indicated that there is a growth in CAM. The changing attitudes and growing acceptance inevitably have made a need for CAM practitioners to be more active in establishing true 'professions'. The holistic approach is embraced by many orthodox health practitioners, and we are possibly witnessing the disappearance of boundaries between the two approaches.

The interface between orthodox medicine and complementary therapy in the care of patients with cancer

Contributed by Zoe Neary, RGN, MBRA, Macmillan Head and Neck Nurse Specialist, University Hospital Birmingham NHS Trust; Lecturer in Reflexology, University of Wolverhampton; Reflexologist, Head and Neck Unit, University Hospital Birmingham NHS Trust.

In recent years there has been a dramatic increase in the use of complementary therapy. There is no exception to this trend within cancer care and palliative care settings.

Practitioners of complementary therapy usually take a holistic approach to care, likewise palliative care acknowledges that there has to be an appreciation of emotional, psychological and social factors before a patient's physical symptoms can be understood and eased (Zollman and Thompson, 1999).

Treatment for cancer is sophisticated and increasingly specialised and there are many members in the multidisciplinary team. Treatment options in orthodox medicine include surgery, radiotherapy and chemotherapy, used in different ways and at different stages of the disease (Sikora, 1994).

Despite an upturn in the understanding of cancer and the technology associated with it, there is a greater recognition of its limitations.

When offering treatment options to patients and gaining informed consent, multidisciplinary teams are increasingly mindful of quality of life issues, attempting to balance the benefits of treatment with the risks and consequences. There is also greater understanding of the psychological impact of the diagnosis of cancer on a patient, his or her family and carers.

Over the last few years many orthodox practitioners who previously regarded complementary therapies with suspicion now have a more open philosophy, and indeed multidisciplinary teams involved in the care of cancer patients include members with specialist skills in counselling and psychotherapy; and massage, touch and relaxation techniques.

Massage for the person with cancer

The aim of a complementary therapy service for people with cancer is to assist them in their coping effectiveness while on their cancer journey. A diagnosis of cancer and its treatment induces great anxiety and with this comes tension. Massage therapies can induce deep relaxation gently and non-invasively, the person being treated as a whole in an uncomplicated way. Touch is a vital form of communication that conveys feelings often more effectively than verbal communication (McNamara, 1994). Whether at diagnosis or close to death, touch reduces the sense of isolation. Massage helps people relax and let go, sometimes for the first time in months; it gives them permission to stop and listen to their body, relax and heal, leaving them better able to deal with their cancer treatment programmes.

The integrated approach to cancer care

Cancer patients benefit from a holistic approach to care. Having complementary therapies available within the medical setting lends an element of approval and credibility to the therapies (Bell, 1999; 2000). Patients and carers find reassurance when their medical consultant approves of and refers them to a therapist who understands the treatment they are receiving, the disease process and the anticipated effects of both. Indeed, many therapists working within integrated multidisciplinary teams are qualified in both orthodox and complementary therapies.

References

Bell L (1999/2000) The Integration of Complementary Therapies within Cancer Services. *Holistic Health* **63**: 8–11

BMA (1999) *News release 1st Nov 1999*. From the Public Affairs Division (Full text said to be available at www.bma.org.uk)

FIM (1997) *A Way Forward for the Next 5 Years*. The Foundation for Integrated Healthcare (A discussion document)

FIM (1998) *May 1998 Conference Proceedings, Integrated Healthcare*

FIM (1999) *The Foundation for Integrated Healthcare, Integrated Health Newsletter*, Oct 1999, 2: 3

Makower A (1999) *House of Lords Science & Technology Committee, Sub-committee III, Complementary and Alternative Medicine – Call for Evidence* October, 1999

McNamara P (1994) *Massage for People With Cancer*. The Cancer Support Centre, Wandsworth: 14–15

Sikora K (1994) Foreword. In: McNamara P *Massage for People With Cancer*. The Cancer Support Centre, Wandsworth: 6–7

Zollman C, Thompson E (1999) Complementary Approaches to Palliative Care. In: Faull C, Carter Y, Woof R (eds) *Handbook of Palliative Care*: 333–5

Appendix I

Useful addresses

British **Acupuncture** Council
Park House
206–208 Latimer Road
London W10 6RE
Tel: 0208 735 0400

College of Traditional Chinese
Acupuncture
Tao House
Queensway
Leamington Spa
Warwickshire CV31 3LZ
Tel: 01926 422121

Society of Teachers of the
Alexander Technique
20 London House
266 Fulham Road
London SW10 9EL
Tel: 0207 351 0828

Aromatherapy Organisations Council
PO Box 19834
London SE25 6WF
Tel: 0208 251 7912
Fax: 0208 251 7942
Website: www.aromatherapy-uk.org

International Federation of
Aromatherapists
182 Chiswick High Road
London W4 1TH
Tel: 0208 742 2606
Fax: 0208 8742 2606

Register of Qualified **Aromatherapists**
PO Box 3431
Danbury
Chelmsford
Essex CM3 4UA
Tel: 01245 227957
E-mail: admin@rqa-uk.org
Website: www.rqa-uk.org

The Institute of Traditional Herbal
Medicine & **Aromatherapy** (ITHMA)
12 Prentices Lane
Woodbridge
Suffolk IP12 4LF
Tel: 01394 388 386
Fax: 01394 388 209
E-mail: info@aromatherapy-studies.com
Website: www.aromatherapy-studies.com

Viv Hinks
Revival **Aromatherapy**
Treatments and Training
45 Avery Rd
Sutton Coldfield
West Midlands B73 6QB
Tel/Fax: 0121 355 1554
E-mail: revivalaroma@aol.com

The Dr. Edward **Bach** Centre
Mount Vernon
Sotwell
Wallingford
Oxfordshire OX10 0PZ
Tel: 01491 834678

Centre for **Complementary Health
Studies**
University of Exeter
Amory Building
Exeter
Devon EX4 4RJ
Tel: 01392 264445

University of Wolverhampton
Complementary Therapy Studies
School of Health Sciences
62–68 Lichfield Street
Wolverhampton
West Midlands WV1 1SB
Tel: 01902 32 11 44
Fax: 01902 32 11 61

British **Chiropractic** Association
Equity House
29 Whitely Street
Reading
Berkshire RG2 OEG
Tel: 01189 757557

The Scottish **Chiropractic** Association
30 Roseburn Place
Edinburgh EH12 5NX
Scotland
Tel: 0131 346 7500

International Association of **Colour Therapists**
Brook House
Hampton Hill
Avening
Tetbury
Gloucestershire GL8 8NS
Tel: 01453 832150

Companies House
Crown Way
Maindy
Cardiff CF4 3UZ
Wales
Tel: 01222 388588

British **Complementary Medicine** Association
Kensington House
33 Imperial Square
Cheltenham
Gloucestershire GL50 1QZ
Tel: 0845 345 5977
Website: www.bcma.co.uk/
E-mail: info@bcma.co.uk

The Upledger Institute UK (**Craniosacral** Therapy)
52 Main Street
Perth PH2 7HB
Scotland
Tel: 01738 444404

The Karuna Institute
Craniosacral Biodynamics
Natsworthy Manor
Widecombe-in-the-Moor
Newton Abbot
Devon TQ13 7TR
Tel: 01647 221 457

Office of **Data Protection** Registrar
Wycliffe House
Water Lane
Wilmslow
Cheshire SK9 5AF
Tel: 01625 545745

Feng Shui Network International
8 King's Court
Pateley Bridge
Harrogate
North Yorkshire HG3 5JW
Tel: 01423 712868

Medical **Herbalism**
The College of Phytotherapy
Bucksteep Manor
East Sussex BN27 4RJ
Tel: 01323 834800
Fax: 01323 834801

British **Homeopathic** Association
27a Devonshire Street
London W1N 1RJ
Tel: 0207 935 2163

Society of **Homeopaths**
2 Artisan Road
Northampton
Northamptonshire NN1 4HU
Tel: 01604 621400

Scottish College of **Homeopathy**
17 Queens Crescent
Glasgow G4 9BL
Scotland
Tel: 0141 332 3917

HSE (Health & Safety Executive) Books
PO Box 1999
Sudbury
Suffolk CO10 6FS
Tel: 01787 881165
Fax: 01787 313995

HSE Information Centre
Broad Lane
Sheffield
South Yorkshire S3 7HQ
Tel: 0541 545500
Website: http://www.open.gov.uk/

British Hypnotherapy Association
67 Upper Berkeley Street
London W14 7QX
Tel: 0171 723 4443

Central Register of Advanced
Hypnotherapists
28 Finsbury Park Road
London N4 2JX
Tel: 0171 359 6991

Stephen Watling
Ecology Insurance Brokers
Oaklands
Chelmsford
Essex CM3 4SF
Tel: 01245 223871
Fax: 01245 222152

Foundation of Integrated Medicine
International House
59 Compton Road
London N1 2YT
Tel: 0207 688 1881
Fax: 0207 688 1882
Website: www.fimed.org

Kinesiology Federation
PO Box 7891
Wimbledon
London SW19 1ZB
Tel: 0208 545 0255

Association of Systematic Kinesiology
39 Browns Road
Surbiton
Surrey KT5 8ST
Tel: 0181 399 3215

Nicola Evans
Evans Whalley Ltd
Marketing Consultants
20 Belwell Lane
Sutton Coldfield
West Midlands B74 4AL
Tel: 0121 323 5330

The British Massage Therapy Council
17 Rymers Lane
Oxford
Oxfordshire OX4 3JU
Tel: 0208 9922554
Website: www.bmtc.co.uk

Northern Institute of Massage
100 Waterloo Road
Blackpool
Lancashire FY4 1AW
Tel: 01253 403548

British Medical Association (BMA)
BMA House
Tavistock Square
London WC1H 9JP
Public affairs div. tel: 0207 383 6473
Website: www.bma.org.uk

General Council and Register of
Naturopaths
Goswell House
2 Goswell Road
Street
Somerset BA16 0JG
Tel: 01458 840072

British Nutrition Foundation
52–54 High Holborn
London WC1V 6RQ
Tel: 0207 404 6504

General Council & Register of **Osteopaths**
56 London Street
Reading
Berkshire RG1 4SQ
Tel: 01189 576585

Osteopathic Information Service
PO Box 2074
Reading
Berkshire RG1 4YR
Tel: 01189 512051

British School of **Osteopathy**
1–4 Suffolk Street
London SW1Y 4HG
Tel: 0207 930 9254

British **Reflexology** Association
Monks Orchard
Whitbourne
Worcestershire WR6 SRB
Tel: 01886 821207
Website: www.britreflex.co.uk

Reiki Alliance
27 Lavington Road
Ealing
London W13 9NN
Tel: 0208 579 3813

The **Research** Council for Complementary
Medicine (RCCM)
505 Riverbank House
1 Putney Bridge Approach
London SW6 3JD
Tel: 0207 384 1772
Fax: 0207 384 1736
Website: www.rccm.org.uk

The **Shiatsu** Society
5 Foxcote
Wokingham
Berkshire RG11 3PG
Tel: 01189 730836

British School of **Shiatsu Do**
97–99 Seven Sisters Road
London N7 7QP
Tel: 02072 811412

Healthwork UK
National Training Organisation
344–354 Gray's Inn Road
London WC1X 8BP
Tel: 0207 692 5550

Appendix II

Legal aspects

The British Complementary Medicine Association Code of Conduct (extracts)

1. Introduction

1.4: Regulations governing Doctors: Doctors are required to comply with the General Medical Council's ethical rules. Since 1991, they have been allowed to delegate patient care to therapists such as BCMA's only if two conditions are met:
The Doctor remains in charge of the case, and
The Doctor is satisfied as to the competence of the practitioner.

1.5: Need for Regulation of Complementary Therapies: The legality of the practice of orthodox medicine in the UK is well established and Osteopaths and Chiropractors are licensed by Parliament. Other Complementary therapists who offer treatment should be able to convince the Medical Profession, the Government and the Courts of Justice if sued of the efficacy and safety of their treatment.

2. Standards for Members and their Practitioners

(a) Relationship with the Client

2.1: Practitioners shall have respect for the religious, spiritual, political and social views of any individual irrespective of race, colour, creed or sex and must never seek to impose their beliefs on a client.

2.2: Practitioners shall at all times conduct themselves in an honourable and courteous manner and with due diligence in their relations with their clients and the public.

2.4: Proper moral conduct must always be paramount in practitioners' relations with clients. They must behave with courtesy, respect, dignity, discretion and tact. Their attitude must be competent and sympathetic, hopeful and positive, thus encouraging an uplift in the client's mental outlook and belief in a progression towards good health practices.

2.9: Practitioners, and all those who work with them, must not disclose (or allow to be disclosed) any information about a client (including the fact of his/her attendance) to any third party, including members of the patient's own family, without the patient's consent unless it is required by due process of the law or for the immediate protection of or avoidance of identifiable real risk to a third party, in which case the practitioner is advised to obtain legal advice.

(c) Administration/Publicity

2.25: All practitioners of member organisations of the BCMA must ensure that their names appear on an approved public register of practitioners of their therapy held by the association to which they belong. This confirms that they are fully qualified to practise and that the organisation to which they belong abides by the BCMA Code of Conduct and Disciplinary Procedure. Their membership of such organisation, and its address, should be displayed in their place of practise.

2.26: Practitioners must ensure they keep clear, comprehensive and dated records of their treatments and advice given. This is especially important for the defence of any negligence actions as well as for efficient and careful practice.

(d) Guidelines for working with other Healthcare Professionals

2.33: Practitioners must recognise that where a client is delegated to them by a Registered Medical Practitioner, the GP remains clinically accountable for the client and for the care offered by the practitioner.

Appendix III

Legal aspects

International Federation of Aromatherapists
Code of Practice

1. Introduction

The aim of the Code of Practice is to set out the basic standards that the International Federation of Aromatherapists expects its members to maintain. This code of practice lays down minimum standards necessary for members of the Federation. Clients who attend a registered aromatherapist expect a professional approach by the practitioner and this professionalism should be reflected in the equipment, furniture and premises.

2. Insurance

Adequate public liability and professional insurance must be held by all practising members.

3. Premises

a) Consultation and treatment rooms must be clean, adequately lit, properly ventilated and in a good state of general repair.

b) A wash basin with hot and cold water supply and properly connected to public drainage is essential and should be located in the work area. Soap, preferably containing antiseptic, and some means of hand-drying should be available.

c) If the consultation and treatment room are not directly accessible from the street, all entrance ways and stairways should be adequately lit.

d) An appropriate sign indicating that an aromatherapist is in practice may be placed at the main entrance.

4. Personal Hygiene

The aromatherapist must ensure that their health and personal hygiene are such as to cause no danger to a client. The practitioner must not eat, drink or smoke while at practice. The aromatherapist must be aware of the elements of public hygiene and local safety by-laws and specifications in connection with aromatherapy.

5. Furniture

a) Massage couches and chairs etc. must be sturdy and safe. They should be kept clean and disinfected.

b) Table tops and other work surfaces must have an impervious surface that can be cleaned and disinfected at each session.

6. Client Register

A card index or other suitable means should be set up to register client's names, addresses and other relevant information including dates of attendance.

If good records are maintained, continuity of client care is possible and case history information can be made available to another aromatherapist if the client moves away from a practice.

A standard card is useful and this should include up-dated progress reports and records of any referrals and tests carried out by other practitioners and should be capable of being understood by any other member taking over or assisting in the care of that client. It is important that the client signs the initial circulation notes.

7. Important notes

a) It is the responsibility of the practising aromatherapist to observe any local by-laws with regard to the therapy undertaken. All necessary legal (pharmaceutical and cosmetic) requirements must be complied with in regard to all materials used and stored, purchased complete or assembled and labelled on practice premises.

b) The Federation expects members not to presume a specialised knowledge outside their own training. Members must be wary of giving advice of skin and bodily ailments outside the limitations of their own specialised knowledge.

c) How the essential oils are used for any particular client is the responsibility of the individual aromatherapist, who must bear in mind his or her own standard of training and level of knowledge plus any professional indemnity insurance requirements.

8. Liaison with other professions

Liaison with the client's doctor may increase better understanding between individual aromatherapists and their local doctors. Gradually, if contact can become established with a number of consultants in various spheres, eg. dermatology, homeopathy, dietetics, reflexology etc., clients' conditions may be greatly assisted, the standing of aromatherapy enhanced and more satisfactory conclusions be attained. Many doctors are co-operative if asked if they would be agreeable to receiving referrals and every such liaison serves to strengthen the ideals that we seek to achieve. By lecturing to other professional bodies and by increasing contact, greater awareness of aromatherapy aims and objectives can be communicated.

9. Controls on PR advertising and articles promoting the IFA

An IFA member who wishes to advertise, promote or give a press release will submit their promotion to the Council before publication. This will enable the Council to keep a high standard on the promotions scene, safeguarding from any misinterpretation and stopping the use of the Federation's name for personal or commercial promotion. All such material should be sent to the Secretary six weeks prior to printing and publishing.

Appendix IV

Relevant legislation

Misrepresentations Act, 1967

Health and Safety at Work Act, 1974

Race Relations Act, 1976

Sex Discrimination, 1976

Consumer Safety Act, 1978

Sales of Goods Act 1979

Health and Safety (First Aid) Regulations, 1981

Local Government, 1982

Supply of Goods and Services, 1982

Fair Trading Act, 1983

Data Protection Act, 1984

Gas Safety (Installation and Use), 1984

Reporting of Injuries, Diseases and Dangerous Occurrences Regulations, 1985

Consumer Protection Act, 1987

Copyright/Performance Rights, 1988

Employers Liability, 1988

Control of Substances Hazardous to Health Regulations, 1988/89

Cosmetic Products (Safety) Regulations, 1989

The Children's Act, 1989

Electricity at Work Regulations, 1989

Environment Act, 1990

Management of Health and Safety at Work, 1992

Manual Handling Operations Regulations, 1992

Trade Union and Employment Rights, 1993

Fire Precautions in the Workplace Regulations, 1997

Working Time Regulations, 1998

Appendix V

Higher education institutions

Higher education institutions providing higher education programmes in complementary therapies 2000/2001

Anglo-European College of Chiropractic
Chiropractic sciences/chiropractic

Bradford College
Complementary therapies

British College of Naturopathy & Osteopathy
Naturopathic medicine
Osteopathic medicine

The British School of Osteopathy
Osteopathy

University of Cardiff
Phytotherapy (herbal medicine)

University of Central Lancashire
Health sciences for complementary medicine
Herbal medicine
Homeopathic medicine

University of Exeter
Various courses in complementary health studies, including postgraduate programmes

University of Glamorgan
Human sciences (chiropractic)

University of Greenwich
Complementary therapies (aromatherapy)
Complementary therapies (stress management)

Liverpool John Moores University
Diploma in aromatic medicine

Middlesex University
Herbal medicine
Traditional Chinese Medicine
Osteopathy

Nescot
Osteopathic medicine

Oxford Brookes
Complementary therapies (aromatherapy)

University of Portsmouth
Natural and complementary medicine

Queen Margaret University College Edinburgh
Complementary medicine

University of Salford
Complementary medicine and health sciences
Complementary therapies

South Bank University
Aromatherapy

University of Westminster
Health sciences: chiropractic, complementary therapies, herbal medicine, homeopathy, nutritional therapy, therapeutic bodywork, Traditional Chinese Medicine, acupuncture, osteopathy

University of Wolverhampton
Complementary therapies: generic
Complementary therapies: aromatherapy
Complementary therapies: reflexology

For information on all of the above Higher Education courses, applications and general enquiries contact:

UCAS
UCAS Fulton House
Jessop Avenue
Cheltenham
Gloucestershire GL50 3SH
Tel: 01242 227788
E-mail: enq@ucas.ac.uk
Website: www.ucas.ac.uk

Index

T

taxes 22
training cost comparison 15
training in aromatherapy 16–17
treatment room 31
     general health and safety 83

U

university
     courses 95, 109

V

venue 31
Vocational Awards International 18

W

working at home 32
     advantages 32
     disadvantages 32